PHYSICAL LAWS
AND EFFECTS

General Electric Series

WRITTEN FOR THE ADVANCEMENT OF

ENGINEERING PRACTICE

PHYSICAL LAWS AND EFFECTS
by C. F. Hix, Jr., and R. P. Alley

ECONOMIC OPERATION OF POWER SYSTEMS
by Leon K. Kirchmayer

DIGITAL COMPUTER PROGRAMMING
by D. D. McCracken

THE ART AND SCIENCE OF PROTECTIVE RELAYING
by C. Russell Mason

APPLIED ELECTRICAL MEASUREMENT
by Isaac F. Kinnard

AIRCRAFT GAS TURBINES
by C. W. Smith

AN INTRODUCTION TO POWER SYSTEM ANALYSIS
by Federick S. Rothe

D-C POWER SYSTEMS FOR AIRCRAFT
by R. H. Kaufmann and H. J. Finison

TRANSIENTS IN POWER SYSTEMS
by Harold A. Peterson

SERVOMECHANICS AND REGULATING SYSTEM DESIGN, TWO VOLUMES
by Harold Chestnut and Robert W. Mayer

TRANSFORMER ENGINEERING
by the late L. F. Blume, A. Boyajian, G. Camilli, T. C. Lennox, S. Minneci, and V. M. Montsinger, Second Edition

CIRCUIT ANALYSIS OF A-C POWER SYSTEMS, TWO VOLUMES
by Edith Clarke

CAPACITORS FOR INDUSTRY
by W. C. Bloomquist, C. R. Craig, R. M. Partington, and R. C. Wilson

PROTECTION OF TRANSMISSION SYSTEMS AGAINST LIGHTNING
by W. W. Lewis

MAGNETIC CONTROL OF INDUSTRIAL MOTORS
by Gerhart W. Heumann, Second Edition

POWER SYSTEM STABILITY
Volume I—Steady State Stability; Volume II—Transient Stability;
by Selden B. Crary

MATERIALS AND PROCESSES
by J. F. Young, Second Edition

ELECTRIC MOTORS IN INDUSTRY
by D. R. Shoults and C. J. Rife; edited by T. C. Johnson

PHYSICAL LAWS
AND EFFECTS

C. F. HIX, JR.

Missile and Space Vehicle Department
General Electric Company
Philadelphia, Pennsylvania

R. P. ALLEY

General Purpose Control Department
General Electric Company
Bloomington, Illinois

*One of a series written by General Electric authors
for the advancement of engineering practice*

JOHN WILEY & SONS, INC., NEW YORK

CHAPMAN & HALL, LTD., LONDON

This compilation is dedicated to

Patsy Hix

without whose patience, stenographic,
and literary help, it would never have
reached this stage.

7479

PREFACE

This compilation contains many common as well as uncommon phenomena which may be of interest to the engineer. It was formulated originally to broaden the scope of the younger engineer, but has found use as a quick reference source for experienced engineers and scientists. Under the circumstances the descriptions given are intended to be as cryptic as possible. The format in general is thus keyed to a short description, an illustration, an indication of the expected magnitude (where this adds to clarity), and lastly a reference or two that will be useful in gaining additional information. (The stated references are the most recent editions, except where the later ones have omitted the pertinent coverage.) To be of maximum use, the entire collection is indexed alphabetically by (1) names; (2) physical quantities involved; and (3) fields of science.

C. F. HIX, JR.

R. P. ALLEY

November, 1958

CONTENTS

A Use for the Compilation of Laws and Effects

C. F. Hix, Jr.

New products, new inventions, innovations, and whole new industries often originate from an idea inspired by an unusual law or effect. Engineers and scientists are making startling advances through added understanding of physical laws and effects. For example, the magnetostriction phenomenon was written off as a laboratory curiosity in 1926. Today, it has been applied to Sonar, strain gages, phonograph pickups, and dust precipitation. Recent work in atomic physics and semi-conductors has seen dozens of laws and effects applied to solve problems outside the laboratory.

More and more present-day problems are demanding a completely new approach or invention in order to advance the art. A fruitful area to search for new approaches is among the multitude of unheralded phenomena existing in nature. But a serious barrier arises at the early state of technical planning—how can information be obtained on little-known laws and effects?

A lesson might be derived from some inventors who keep a card file of all the effects they hear about. The primary sources of this material for those inventors of the author's acquaintance are the early editions of old physics books. Even the later texts have an astounding repertoire, though they tend toward more general presentations. Of course, the latest additions to this field of knowledge are found in the current scientific journals, and technical dictionaries provide a broad coverage of their own particular field. But none of these sources gives a complete

1

or convenient coverage. Unfamiliar and unapplied laws and effects are scattered and buried among a mountain of books and magazines.

This book was compiled so that a search of laws and effects could become a practical part of the engineering approach to problems. This collection has been indexed and cross referenced so that pertinent information may be located rapidly. Here are a few techniques which will assure maximum results.

First of all, for the purposes of this text let us define the difference between a law and an effect. A stated effect is a reaction in nature observed when a certain stimulus is supplied. Frequently, the exact reasons connecting this cause and effect are not understood. The data on effects are often empirical and difficult to handle in a mathematical analysis. This doesn't say, however, that a once-named effect can't or won't be understood as the science of the day becomes more sophisticated.

On the other hand, a law is an interpretation of one or more effects and is generalized to make a complete understanding possible. Problems involving laws can be treated analytically. Galileo described the speed of a falling body as proportional to time squared. Newton further generalized on Galileo's observation and stated the law of gravitation.

An excellent technique for utilizing this compilation of laws and effects in problem solution is to break the problem into input and output physical quantities. As a simple example, you may want a light signal input and a temperature variation output. First, try bridging the gap directly with any known effect. If this is unsuccessful, think of a number of physical quantities that are suggestive as intermediate steps. Light might be converted to resistance, to current, to heat. These steps may be connected with as many different phenomena as can be recalled from memory. A number of semi-complete paths will result, each with a different link missing. A renewed search of unfamiliar laws and effects is certain to complete one or more of these links. The Cross Reference by Physical Quantities provides an easy means for finding related effects.

This book can be entered by two other channels: the Index and the Cross Reference by Fields of Science. The Index serves the purpose of a technical dictionary. *Even though the laws and effects are alphabetically arranged, the Index should be consulted since there are often many different names for the same effect.* The Cross Reference by Fields of Science permits a clearer picture to be gained of a particular field.

Mr. Albert Hansen, Jr., of General Electric's Instrument Department, recently carried to fruition a development which demonstrates the application of laws and effects. He was assigned the problem of developing a precision potentiometer of the self-balancing servo type. After studying the prior art, he determined that a superior form of d-c to a-c converter would be a substantial technical contribution to the art. In nearly every case, converters employed by others in the field used contacts to convert the low level d-c error signal (about 10–13 microwatts) to a-c for amplification. Mr. Hansen made a search of all known laws and effects involving physical quantities that could be used to modulate such a low level d-c signal. The Hall effect was found and offered a distinct possibility, provided that materials were available with a sufficiently high Hall constant. (See Hall Effect.) Tellurium was first found in the literature to have the highest coefficient available. By one of those fortunate accidents that happen to a person earnestly seeking an answer, data were found on germanium in connection with mobility studies in semi-conductors that showed it to have an extremely high Hall coefficient as well. Immediately a sample of germanium was obtained and a model constructed that proved to be superior to any known method of d-c to a-c conversion. The result was an entirely static device. A fundamental U. S. patent has been issued on this converter.

The possibilities for new applications of a law are never exhausted. Electrostatic paint spraying uses Coulomb's law; the object to be painted is one electrode, the paint gun the other. A scheme might be developed to spray oil into a furnace by the same method, eliminating the air blower used for atomization of fuel. The "state of the art" is constantly being changed by engineers with indomitable curiosity, imagination, perseverance, and a background of laws and effects. Among the problems being attacked are an accurate vertical reference for aircraft and missiles, fusion power, ways of controlling friction, high temperature electrical components, and methods of electrically connecting and mechanically mounting components by a means that is not bigger than the components themselves. A knowledge of laws and effects demands a recognition of exceptions and limitations. The exceptions are just as valuable as the rule. For example, the inverse temperature resistance characteristic of certain materials is used to make thermistors and to provide protective circuits in electric blankets. The unusual temperature resistance behavior near absolute zero has already been applied outside the laboratory. The exceptions often turn up when pressing the stated equations beyond their intent, for the laws in the extremes do not always follow generalized equations. Limitations, on the other hand, present serious pitfalls to the unwary. The failure to investigate and analyze orders of magnitude can lead to many wasted development dollars. For instance, the Peltier effect states that a junction of two dissimilar metals will absorb heat when current flows through the joint in the proper direction. This suggests the possibility of a refrigerator with no moving parts. However, as the current flow is increased to get more cooling, the generation of resistance heat becomes significant. The net result is that under best conditions the junction will cool 10°C below ambient for all except special semiconductor combinations. (See Thermoelectric Effects.)

A good background in basic laws and effects has another more subtle advantage. Possible trouble areas can be foreseen in the early development stages of a project. In the design of a very accurate aircraft instrument, trouble developed when mysterious voltages appeared in the output signal on subjecting the instrument to vibrations. If the design engineer had been aware of the Thermoelastic effect, the production of an electrical potential between two points in stressed metal, he could have avoided several false starts in his design. The existence of a significant but unexpected effect is often discovered late in the testing stage of development. Any development-minded engineer should give serious consideration to building a compilation of laws and effects for himself; these can only be collected over a period of years through a constant awareness. No two people's interests are exactly alike; one person may choose to collect from the optical area, while the other may have need from the electronic field. One should also consider seriously collecting from related fields of interest. If one could search out the effects of any one field, compile an explanation interrelating them, and illustrate them with examples, he would have a sound understanding and a text book in that field. *The authors are continuing to build their compilation, for this text is by no means complete nor is it intended to be.*

This compilation of laws and effects is a useful tool as a dictionary, a thought stimulator, and problem approach tool. The Index is the first step in locating a law or effect in this book; even though the main compilation is alphabetically arranged, there are many different names for the same or related effect.

Laws and effects, to be of any value, must be collected. The continued building of background knowledge which is well assimilated provides ammunition for the mind to utilize in problem synthesis.

Index of Physical Laws
and Effects*

* Also see page 267 for additional entries.

5

Description of the Laws
and Effects

ABSORPTION

I. Description

Materials absorb all wavelengths of electromagnetic radiation to some extent. If the materials attenuate the radiation severely over a considerable frequency band, its absorption is general. If the absorption occurs primarily on narrow bands, the process is known as selective absorption.

As is true for all radiation, the energy is absorbed in quanta. The quanta absorbed may be used to change the energy of the material in several general ways:

1. A change in the nuclear state of the atom (gamma rays)

2. A shift in the quantum state of an electron (light, ultraviolet).

3. A change in the vibration amplitude of two nuclei (near infrared).

4. A change in the rotational kinetic energy of the molecule (far infrared).

The excited atoms lose their energy either by collision (heat) or re-radiation.

II. Illustration

The energy absorbed by a body is usually used to raise the temperature of the material. The energy reflected or transmitted, if in the visible region, is interpreted by the eye as color. Some unusual aspects of
absorption are resonance radiation and fluorescence. Resonance radiation (primarily occurring in gases) is the scattering of the incident light
in all directions as the material first absorbs the incident energy, then
re-radiates some of it on the same wavelength. This resonance radiation is very pronounced with sodium vapor. Fluorescence is the re-
radiation of the energy on a longer wavelength.

Very dilute solutions of some chemicals may strongly absorb narrow
bands of frequencies, thus allowing a chemical analysis by optical
means.

III. References

1. MacDougall, Frank H., *Physical Chemistry*, The Macmillan
   Co., New York, 3rd Ed., 1952, pp. 208–212. Description of absorption.

   See also Lambert's Law, Luminescence, Stoke's Law of Fluorescence, Wood and Ellett Effect.

Quantities

Absorption	Chemical composition	Energy (K.E.)	Light
Amplitude	Color	Frequency	

ADSORPTION

I. Description

Adsorption is the ability of a material to hold a gas or liquid on its surface. This attraction may be molecular as with charcoal or capillary as with silica gel.

Adsorption is also affected by the surface tension of the solute. There will be a positive adsorption if the solute lowers the surface tension, whereas there will be a negative adsorption of the solute in the surface layer if, by adding solute to the solution, the surface tension is increased.

II. Illustration

Silica gel is used to remove water vapor from an atmosphere (dehydrator). Certain metals such as platinum black have the power to gather gases on their surface. Since this action is exothermic, platinum black has been used to ignite gas burners. Hydrogen absorbed on platinum is electrically conducting and is used as a hydrogen electrode. Adsorption has also been used in some refrigerative systems. Of interest is the diamagnetism exhibited by adsorbed paramagnetic materials, even though the adsorber (charcoal) may have been initially slightly paramagnetic.

III. Magnitude

A feeling for the magnitude can be had by examination of the empirical expression. For equilibrium between a gas or vapor and a solid (the Freundlich equation):

$$x = AP^n$$

where x = the amount of gas adsorbed per unit area of the solid
   n = a constant (usually between 0 and 1)
   P = the partial pressure of gas in equilibrium
   A = area

IV. References

1. Macintyre, H. J., and F. W. Hutchinson, *Refrigeration Engineering*, John Wiley and Sons, New York, 2nd Ed., 1950, p. 113. Primarily a qualitative discussion.
2. MacDougall, Frank H., *Physical Chemistry*, The Macmillan Co., New York, 1952, 3rd Ed., pp. 708–712. Treatments for liquids and solids.

See also Surface Tension.

Quantities

Chemical composition   Concentration   Gas   Surface tension

AMPÈRE'S LAW

I. Description

When a conductor carries an electric current in a magnetic field, there is a force on the conductor that is proportional to the current, the length of the conductor in the magnetic field, the magnetic flux density, and the sine of the angle between the conductor and the magnetic field. The force is at right angles to both the conductor and the magnetic field. A charged particle moving with some velocity V through a magnetic field acts the same as a current and will experience a force in the same manner.

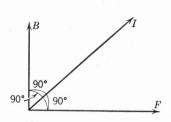

A nonsophisticated way of remembering the relationship between these parameters is stated by Fleming's rule, which relates flux, motion, and emf. The index finger, middle finger, and thumb are placed at right angles to each other and represent flux, emf, and motion, respectively. If the right hand is used, these are the conditions as found in the generator, while the left hand is used to analyze behavior of a motor.

II. Illustration

Ampère's law can be used as a basis for measuring the current in a conductor. The conductor would be placed normal to the magnetic field of known flux density. The force, which could be measured by sensitive balance, would be proportional to the current in the conductor. The effect of the magnetic field on a moving charged particle is used by the mass spectrometer for chemical analysis.

III. Magnitude

The expression for the force on a current-carrying conductor is as follows:

$$F = \frac{BIL \sin \theta}{10}$$

where F = force in dynes
I = current in amp
L = length in cm
B = flux density in gauss
θ = angle between V and L

This formula may be rewritten for use in motors:

$$T = K_t Z I_a \phi$$

where T = torque
K_t = constant involving number of paths, poles, and units
Z = number of conductors on armature
I_a = current to armature
ϕ = flux from one north pole entering armature

The equivalent expression for the case of the moving charge is as follows:

$$F = \frac{VQB \sin \alpha}{10}$$

where F = force in dynes
   Q = charge in coulombs
   V = velocity in cm per sec
   B = flux density in gauss
   α = angle between B and the velocity

If the current of 1 amp flows in a conductor 5 cm long normal to a field of 10,000 gauss, the conductor would experience a force of 0.011 lb (5000 dynes).

At Cambridge, Mass., the magnitude of the earth's field is 0.58 gauss. If, at this location, a single coil enclosing an area of 1 square meter had a current of 25 amp circulated through it, the maximum torque due to the earth's field would be 0.001 lb-ft.

IV. References

1. Sears, F. W., *Principle of Physics,* Addison-Wesley Publishing Co., Cambridge, Mass., 1951, Vol. 2, p. 240.
2. M.I.T. Staff, *Electric Circuits,* John Wiley and Sons, New York, 1940, p. 29.
3. Hausmann, E., and E. Slack, *Physics,* D. Van Nostrand Co., New York, 3rd Ed., 1948. "Force of Current Carrying Wire," pp. 426–428; "Action of Field on Moving Charge," p. 435.
4. Attwood, Stephen S., *Electric and Magnetic Fields,* John Wiley and Sons, New York, 3rd Ed., 1949. Field about a moving charge. Effect of relativity.
5. Richtmyer, F. K., and E. H. Kennard, *Introduction to Modern Physics,* McGraw-Hill Book Co., New York, 5th Ed., 1955. Field due to an accelerated charge.

Quantities

Angle	Force	Potential
Charge	Length	Velocity
Current	Magnetic flux	

AMPÈRE'S (BIOT-SAVART) LAW

(Sometimes termed Laplace's law)

I. Description

Ampère's law furnishes the basis for the solution of low-frequency problems relating to the magnetic fields produced by electric currents. Since a magnetic field exists in a region where a magnetic pole experiences a mechanical force, it may be concluded that whenever a current of electricity flows, a magnetic field exists in the region of the current and it is possible to measure the value of the field by placing a magnet in that region. The field intensity (H) is by definition equal to the force per unit magnetic pole $(F \div M)$.

II. Illustration

The relation is most applicable to the design of magnetic fields of a desired pattern. By the use of the so-called Helmholtz coils, a magnetic field may be obtained that is nearly uniform over a limited region near the center of the coil.

More familiar applications are electromagnets, solenoids, a number of electrical instruments, and magnetic deflection coils for television receivers.

III. Magnitude

To compute the field intensity at some point (P) due to a current (i) following any path, it is desirable to know the portion of the intensity at (P) due to the current in an element (dx) of the path. Since it is impossible to isolate an element of current, Ampère formulated the following mathematical relation entirely on the basis of experience and reasoning:

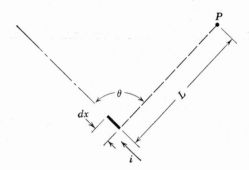

$$d\,H_p = \frac{i\,dx\,\sin\theta}{10L^2}$$

where H_p = field intensity at P (oersteds)

i = current (amp)

dx = element of current (cm)

L = distance from dx to P (cm)

θ = angle between direction of i and the line L

The direction of the field intensity at P is perpendicular to the plane which contains the element dx and line L (right hand rule, Ampère's law).

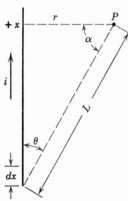

With this relation it is possible to determine field intensity existing at a point in the vicinity of a current following a known path by integrating over the current path.

The magnetic intensity at a point due to a current flowing in straight wire of infinite length is given by:

$$H = \int_{-\infty}^{+\infty} \frac{i\,dx}{10L^2}\sin\theta$$

But $x = r\tan\alpha$

$dx = r\sec^2\alpha\,d\alpha$

$$L = \frac{r}{\cos\alpha}$$

$$\sin\theta = \cos\alpha$$

$$H = \frac{i}{10r} \int_{-\pi/2}^{+\pi/2} \cos\alpha\,d\alpha$$

$$H = \frac{2i}{10r}$$

So for $i = 1.0$ amp, $r = 1$ cm

$H = 0.2$ oersted

IV. References

1. Page, Leigh, *Introduction to Theoretical Physics,* D. Van Nostrand Co., New York, 1952, pp. 426–444. Theoretical treatment of several cases. (Electric currents—Ampère's law.)
2. Hausmann, E., and E. Slack, *Physics,* D. Van Nostrand Co., New York, 3rd Ed., 1948, pp. 422–423. A more elementary presentation than that of the first reference.

Quantities

    Angle   Current   Length   Magnetic flux

ARCHIMEDES' PRINCIPLE

I. Description

A body immersed in a fluid experiences buoyant force equal to the weight of the displaced fluid (either liquid or gas). The pressure exerted by fluids on surfaces in contact with them is perpendicular to each surface area element. The buoyant force is a static force on the body and is exerted upward and through the center of gravity of the displaced fluid. This point of action is called the center of buoyancy.

II. Illustration

A hydrometer gives a direct measure of the density of a fluid. The volume of the floating object that is submerged is directly proportional to the density of the fluid. The load capacity of balloons is limited by this principle.

III. Magnitude

It is possible by proper construction to obtain readings of four significant figures on even simple hydrometers.

IV. References

1. Hausmann, E., and E. Slack, *Physics*, D. Van Nostrand Co., New York, 3rd Ed., 1948, pp. 200, 202–203, and 233. The principles for both fluids and gases with examples.

Quantities

Density   Mass   Specific gravity   Volume

ARRHENIUS THEORY OF ELECTROLYTIC DISSOCIATION

I. Description

In 1788, Blagden (as well as Watson at a slightly earlier date) pointed to an effect on the freezing point of a solvent by the concentration of solute present. In 1886, J. H. van't Hoff developed the theoretical treatment of freezing point depression. In 1887, Arrhenius proposed a theory that was in part to explain Blagden's (and Watson's) effect.

Theory of electrolytic dissociation states that the molecule of an electrolyte can give rise to two or more electrically charged atoms or ions; i.e., particles are present in greater number than would be normally expected from the mass of substance dissolved, thereby causing an abnormally greater effect on the boiling points, freezing points, etc., observed in aqueous solutions of inorganic acids, bases, and salts.

II. Illustration

The depression of the freezing point of water by various materials is used to prevent the cooling systems of internal combustion engines from freezing during the winter months.

III. Magnitude

A molal (1 gram molecular weight in 1000 cc H_2O) sugar solution (a non-electrolyte) freezes at $-1.86°C$, while on the other hand a molal solution of sodium chloride (an electrolyte) freezes at $-3.42°C$. The theory applies fairly well to weak electrolytes, but not at all well to strong electrolytes, which may display up to four times the effect expected on the basis of molal concentration alone.

IV. References

1. MacDougall, Frank H., *Physical Chemistry*, The Macmillan Co., New York, 3rd Ed., 1952, pp. 270–274. Theory and validity.
2. Dole, Malcolm, *Principles of Experimental and Theoretical Electro-Chemistry*, McGraw-Hill Book Co., New York, 1935, pp. 8–23. History and description.

See also Raoult's Law, Le Châtelier's Law.

Quantities

Boiling point   Chemical composition   Freezing point

BARKHAUSEN EFFECT

I. Description

Over the middle portion of the *B-H* curve of an iron sample, a step-wise build-up of flux density *B* is observed as an applied field is smoothly increased in intensity. This build-up is by finite jumps.

This effect is most readily explained by and used to substantiate the domain theory of magnetization. As the applied field is increased beyond very small values, the magnetic moments of individual domains are aligned in the direction of the preferred crystal axis nearest to that of the impressed field. This effect takes place, not by realignment of the domain as a rigid body, but by realignment of the axis of the spins of the individual electrons within the domain from one stable direction to another stable direction. Throughout any one domain, this realignment of spins takes place simultaneously.

II. Illustration

The fact that the change in magnetization occurs in jumps can be observed by means of a loudspeaker connected to a coil surrounding the specimen. Each reorientation of a domain suddenly changes the flux through the pickup coil and causes a click in the loudspeaker.

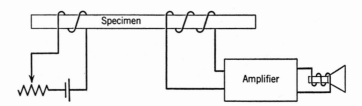

III. Magnitude

The jump in flux density per any one step is in the order of 10^{-6} gauss. The effect is strongest in single crystals of silicon steel.

IV. References

1. Bozorth, R. M., "Present Status of Ferromagnetic Theory," *A.I.E.E. Transactions,* 1935, Vol. 54, pp. 1251–1261. Review of magnetic theory and progress.
2. M. I. T. Staff, *Magnetic Circuits and Transformers,* John Wiley and Sons, New York, 1943, pp. 11–12. Limitations of Barkhausen effect.

Quantities

Inductance   Magnetic flux   Permeability   Sound

BAUSCHINGER EFFECT

I. Description

This effect is the low deformation resistance in compression following a tensile prestrain. This effect is greater at room temperatures than at higher ones.

II. Illustration

This effect may be noticed during a series of tests where compression follows the application of a tensile stress. The material does not follow the usual stress-strain curve immediately upon the application of the load.

III. Magnitude

Upon reapplication of the load to the specimen, the strain may be as much as 0.1% greater than expected (for copper). This effect deals with plastic deformation.

IV. References

1. Lubahn, J. D., *The Bauschinger Effect in Creep and Tensile Tests on Copper,* General Electric Research Laboratory Report RL-872, Research Publications Services, The Knolls, Schenectady, New York. Experiments with copper.

Quantities

Force	Strain	Temperature
Length	Stress	Yield point

BERNOULLI'S THEOREM

I. Description

At any point along a tube through which a liquid is flowing, the sum of the pressure plus the potential energy due to position plus the kinetic energy remains constant (friction being disregarded).

II. Illustration

Bernoulli's law states that if the flow takes place without any external interference, that is, without doing work or having work done on it, then the total head H remains unchanged throughout the flow; a fact which follows from the principle of conservation of energy. Use is made of this Bernoulli effect in a venturi to measure flow; also, air-foils obtain lift because of this theory. Some forms of liquid helium violate this law.

There is a combined effect of boundary layer drag and Bernoulli's theorem on rotating spheres and cylinders. The stream in which the body is rotating exerts a considerable force at right angles to the mean flow direction, and this is sometimes referred to as the Magnus effect. This effect can be seen when a tennis ball is "sliced" in play, and a thrown "curved" baseball. Attempts have been made to apply the Magnus effect to obtaining lift on rotating cylinders for the propulsion of ships. This is known as the Flettner rotor or Flettner principle.

III. Magnitude

If no external forces, other than gravity, act on the unit of volume considered, then its total energy must remain constant. Expressed mathematically:

$$H = h + \frac{P}{\rho g} + \frac{v^2}{2g}$$

where H = total head (cm)
  h = elevation above datum plane (cm)
  P = static pressure (dynes per cm²)
  ρ = density (grams/cm³)
  g = gravitational constant (cm per sec²)
  v = velocity (cm per sec)

In hydraulics, the three terms or the three members of the Bernoulli equation are called respectively the elevation head, the pressure head, and the velocity head.

Torricelli's law which describes the velocity of the efflux of a liquid from an orifice in a vessel which is kept filled to a constant level may be derived from the above:

$$v_B{}^2 = 2g(h_A - h_B)$$

where v_B = velocity of the efflux of the liquid B (for a hole at B)
  h_A = height of tank at A (top of liquid)
  h_B = height of tank at B (orifice) or
  $h_A - h_B$ = fluid head available

IV. References

1. Hausmann, E., and E. Slack, *Physics,* D. Van Nostrand Co., New York, 3rd Ed., 1948, pp. 216–217. Derivation, statement, and use.
2. Page, Leigh, *Introduction to Theoretical Physics,* D. Van Nostrand Co., New York, 3rd Ed., 1952, pp. 241–243. Derivation and mathematics of Bernoulli's theorem for an incompressible liquid in steady flow.

Quantities

Density	Energy (P.E.)	Pressure
Energy (K.E.)	Flow	Velocity

BIOT AND FOURIER'S LAW

(Also known as conduction heat transfer or as Fourier's law)

I. Description

The one dimensional form of this law states that the quantity of heat conducted in the x direction of a homogeneous solid in time is a product of the conducting area normal to the flow path, the temperature gradient along the path, and the property of the material known as the thermal conductivity.

II. Illustration

Whenever heat flows by conduction in the transient or unsteady state, the temperature of a fixed point within the material does not remain constant; that is, the temperature within a material undergoing cooling or heating varies with time. Some of the industrial problems which involve this particular type of heat transmission are: the annealing of castings, the vulcanization of rubber, and the heating or cooling of walls of buildings, furnaces, and ovens.

III. Magnitude

The conduction heat transfer through a solid is expressed analytically:

$$\frac{dQ}{d\theta} = -kA \frac{dT}{dx}$$

where Q = quantity of heat
  θ = time
  k = coefficient of thermal conductivity
  A = area normal to path

  $\dfrac{dT}{dx}$ = temperature gradient along the path

in which the negative sign is arbitrarily affixed in order that Q will be positive.

IV. References

1. Schneider, P. J., *Conduction Heat Transfer,* Addison-Wesley Publishing Co., Cambridge, Mass., 1955. Complete treatment of conduction heat transfer.

Quantities

Area   Heat flux   Temperature   Time

BREMSTRAHLUNG RADIATION

I. Description

Continuous spectra X-rays are produced whenever electrons are slowed down by an absorbing medium. This effect may be predicted from Maxwell's equations.

II. Illustration

The production of X-rays by ordinary X-ray tubes or by a betatron illustrates the use of this phenomenon.

III. Magnitude

The proportion of the energy of the electron which is converted into radiation is increased as the initial energy of the electron increases and also with the atomic number of the target material. Bremstrahlung radiation occurs even for gases as target materials.

IV. Reference

1. Glasstone, Samuel, *Sourcebook on Atomic Energy*, D. Van Nostrand Co., New York, 1950, pp. 106–166. Description and some effects.

Quantities

Acceleration	Electric flux	Frequency
Density	Energy (K.E.)	Potential
		Radiation

BREWSTER'S LAW

I. Description

For some angle of reflection from a surface, the reflected and refracted rays contain a maximum of polarized light. This angle of incidence, or the polarizing angle, is the one for which the refracted and reflected rays are at right angles.

II. Illustration

The reflection from a series of thin glass plates is used to produce light which has a high degree of polarization (about 50%). The reflection of light from roads (glare) is largely polarized parallel or horizontally to the road, making vertically polarized sun glasses useful to eliminate this glare.

III. Magnitude

The tangent of the polarizing angle for a substance is equal to the index of refraction. If n is the index of refraction and ϕ is the polarizing angle:

$$n = \tan \phi$$

For glass with a refractive index of 1.5, the theoretical reflection factor for light polarized in the plane of incidence is 0.148, while that for light polarized perpendicular to the plane of incidence is 0. Apparently Brewster's law does not hold exactly to this because reflection is not completely a surface phenomenon. However, six or seven glass plates produce light about 50% polarized.

IV. References

1. Preston, Thomas A., *The Theory of Light,* Macmillan and Co., Ltd., London, 4th Ed., 1929, pp. 345–6. Law and polarization by reflection.

2. Walsh, John W. T., *Photometry*, D. Van Nostrand Co., New York, 2nd Ed., 1953. Calculation of amount and polarization of light reflected.

Quantities

Angle   Index of refraction   Polarization

BROWNIAN MOVEMENT

I. Description

The Brownian movement is seen in colloidal solutions and is supposed to furnish evidence of molecular motion. Small, visible, colloidal particles are knocked about by colliding with the invisible molecules like footballs in the midst of a crowd of invisible players.

When a colloidal solution is viewed through an ultramicroscope, points of light are seen, due to particles which show a trembling or vibrating movement. This was observed first in 1827 by Robert Brown, a botanist.

II. Illustration

The Brownian movement has been used to determine Avogadro's number.

III. Magnitude

A microscope is necessary to observe this motion, the maximum particle size for which this motion can be observed being approximately 0.001 mm.

IV. References

1. Ephrain, Fritz, *Inorganic Chemistry,* translated by P. C. L. Thorne and E. R. Roberts. Interscience Publishers, New York, 1946, pp. 99–111. Relation of Brownian movement and Avogadro's number. (The latest edition is the 6th published by London, Oliver, and Boyd.)
2. MacDougall, Frank H., *Physical Chemistry,* The Macmillan Co., New York, 1950, pp. 704–706. Relation of Brownian movement and Avogadro's number.

Quantities

Temperature   Velocity

CAPACITANCE/DIELECTRIC

I. Description

Capacitance is measured by the charge which must be communicated to a body to raise its potential one unit.

The capacity of a condenser is directly proportional to the dielectric constant of the material separating the conducting surfaces. The dielectric constant of some materials varies with frequency, temperature, applied voltage, and applied stress. (The latter two are known respectively as the electro-optical and the piezo-optical effects.)

II. Illustration

This effect is used to measure fluid heights. The variation of the dielectric constant between the plates as the fluid level changes is interpreted as a variation in liquid height.

III. Magnitude

Electrostatic unit capacitance is that which requires one electrostatic unit of charge to raise the potential one electrostatic unit. The farad $= 9 \times 10^{11}$ electrostatic units. A capacitance of 1 farad requires 1 coulomb of electricity to raise its potential 1 volt.

The capacitance of several common combinations is given below:

Geometry	Capacity (farads)	Symbols
Any body	$C = \dfrac{Q}{V}$	C = capacitance
		Q = charge
		V = volts
Spherical conductor	$C = 4\pi Er$	E = dielectric constant
Two concentric spheres	$C = \dfrac{4\pi E r_1 r_2}{r_2 - r_1}$	r = radius
Two concentric cylinders	$C = \dfrac{2\pi Es}{\log_\epsilon \dfrac{r_2}{r_1}}$	s = distance between or length
Parallel plates	$C = \dfrac{AE}{s}$	A = area

These formulas give capacitance in farads if dimensions are in meters and $E = E_r/36\pi10^9$, where E_r = dielectric constant of the material relative to free space.

These formulas give capacitance in electrostatic units if the dimensions are in centimeters and if $E = K/4\pi$ is used, where K = dielectric constant of the material (free space $= 1$).

The maximum variation of dielectric constant is from several thousand for barium titanate to one for free space.

The change in dielectric constant with frequency may be 3:1 or more; again, this large variation is for ceramic materials.

The variations of dielectric constant with temperature may be 3:1 or more, some types of barium titanate ceramics being very sensitive.

IV. References

1. Attwood, Stephen S., *Electric and Magnetic Fields,* John Wiley and Sons, New York, 1949. Formulas and their derivations for capacitance of simple shapes.
2. Kaplyanski, A. E., "Methods for the Design of Electrical Devices

with Non-linear Dielectrics," *Elektrichestvo,* No. 1, 1953, pp. 44–48. Summary appearing in *The Engineers' Digest,* London, July 1953, Vol. 14, No. 7, pp. 257–260, "The Design and Use of Non-linear Dielectric Materials."

3. U. S. Patent 2,669,692, "Method for Determining Electrical Characteristics of Semi-conducting Bodies," February 16, 1954. Use of barium titanate power to produce visible potential lines over a semi-conductor surface.

Also see Piezoelectric Effects (for additional references).

Quantities

Capacitance	Dielectric constant	Potential
Charge	Length	Temperature

CAVITATION

I. Description

If a pressure change occurs in a fluid so that the local pressure is below the vapor pressure, a bubble of the vapor is formed. This process, the bubble formation, and its subsequent collapse (often violent) is termed cavitation. The local high transient pressures and temperatures produced in cavitation are responsible for most of the observed effects.

II. Illustration

Cavitation may be produced by motion such as in ship propellers, or by sound waves in fluids. Electrical discharges occur because of the potential differences built up on opposite sides of the cavity. Sonoluminescence, the production of light by sound (occurs feebly in water), may result from ultrasonic cavitation in liquids. Some immiscible combinations may be emulsified by cavitation.

III. Magnitude

In water, the hammering action of the cavities collapsing may give rise to local pressures of thousands of atmospheres and temperatures of several hundred degrees. In distilled water, 0.03 watt/cm² or pressure variations of ±0.3 atmosphere are required to produce cavitation.

IV. References

1. Weissler, Alfred, "Sono-chemistry: The Production of Chemical Changes with Sound Waves," *The Journal of the Acoustical Society of America,* Vol. 25, No. 4, July 1953, pp. 651–657. A good survey, mainly concerned with chemical reactions.
2. Willard, G. W., "Ultrasonically Induced Cavitation in Water: A Step by Step Process," *The Journal of the Acoustical Society of America,* Vol. 25, No. 4, July 1953, pp. 669–686. A qualitative discussion.

Quantities

Energy (K.E.)	Sound	Vapor pressure
Pressure	Temperature	Velocity

CHRISTIANSEN EFFECT

I. Description

When finely powdered transparent substances, such as glass or quartz, are immersed in a liquid of the same index of refraction, maximum transparency can be obtained only for monochromatic light. If white light is employed, the transmitted color corresponds to the particular wavelength for which the two substances, solid and liquid, have exactly the same index of refraction. Owing to differences in dispersion the indices of refraction of the solid and liquid will match for only a narrow band of the spectrum.

II. Illustration

When illuminated by the proper color light, a transparent glass or plastic object will become invisible when immersed in a liquid of the same refractive index. Since the refractive indices of some liquids change with temperature, this effect may be used as a temperature detector as well as a selective filter.

III. Magnitude

As an example of the temperature sensitivity of this type filter, crown glass particles in liquid methyl benzoate transmit red light at 64°F and blue light at 122°F. Magnesia powder films may be used in the infrared. Appreciable transmission occurs for bandwidths of about 1000 A.

IV. References

1. Koller, Lewis R., *Ultraviolet Radiation,* John Wiley and Sons, Inc., New York, 1952, p. 173. Use of this effect to construct filters.

2. Strong, John, *Procedures in Experimental Physics,* Prentice-Hall, Englewood Cliffs, New Jersey, 1938, pp. 372–375. Construction, uses, and limitations of Christiansen filter.

Quantities

Color	Light	Temperature
Frequency	Opaqueness	Translucence

COMPTON EFFECT

I. Description

When X-rays fall upon a plate made of some chosen element, the primary X-ray will be either absorbed, or will pass through unaffected, but will also give rise to secondary radiation. The secondary radiation is made up of four parts: (*a*) scattered X-rays, (*b*) characteristic X-rays, (*c*) scattered beta particles, (*d*) characteristic beta particles. The Compton effect is associated with the scattered X-rays known as Thomson scattering.

A large part of the scattered X-rays are of the same wavelength as the primary X-ray, but changed only in direction. These are reported to bounce off atoms. However, when an X-ray strikes an electron, it bounces off (an electron is several thousand times lighter than an atom), imparting some of its energy to the electron. The X-ray in this case has a slightly longer wavelength. This change in wavelength is known as the Compton effect.

II. Illustration

The effect may be explained by the use of the Einstein quantum theory of light. The single X-ray photon, acting as a material particle, may collide with an electron and recoil as though it were a perfectly elastic sphere.

III. Magnitude

Applying the law of conservation of energy to the collision, it is assumed that the energy $(\frac{1}{2}mv^2)$ imported to the recoiling electron must be supplied by the incident X-ray quantum (hf_0). Having lost energy, the X-ray moves off in some new direction with lower frequency (f_1) and energy (hf_1). Applying conservation of energy we have:

$$hf_0 = hf_1 + \frac{1}{2}mv^2$$

where $hf_0 =$ energy of the X-ray before impact
$hf_1 =$ energy of the X-ray after impact
$m =$ mass of the electron (should be corrected for relativistic effects)
$v =$ velocity of recoiling electron

By further manipulation and introducing wavelength, we get the equation for change in wavelength:

$$\Delta\lambda = \frac{h}{m_0 c}(1 - \cos\phi)$$

where $\Delta\lambda =$ change in wavelength
$h =$ Planck's constant
$m_0 =$ mass of electron, or atom collided with
$\phi =$ angle of the scattered photon
$c =$ speed of light

For X-rays that are scattered at an angle of 90°, the observed or calculated change in wavelength amounts to 0.243 A and is the same for all X-ray wavelengths.

IV. References

1. Richtmyer, F. K., and E. H. Kennard, *Introduction to Modern Physics*, McGraw-Hill Book Co., New York, 1955. A qualitative and quantitative description.
2. Kaplan, I., *Nuclear Physics*, Addison-Wesley Publishing Co., Cambridge, Mass., 1955, pp. 102–105. Detailed analysis and description.

Quantities

Absorption   Dispersion   Frequency   Radiation

CONSERVATION LAWS

I. Description

A. *Conservation of Dynamical Energy.* In a conservative field of force, a particle moves in such a manner that the sum of its kinetic and potential energies remain constant.

B. *Conservation of Energy.* Energy can neither be created nor destroyed.*

C. *Conservation of Mass.* The mass of any isolated group of bodies is not changed by physical or chemical interaction.*

D. *Conservation of Mass and Energy.** The sum of mass plus energy remains constant. Mass may be converted to energy and vice versa according to $E = mc^2$.

E. *Conservation of Momentum.* The vector sum of the momenta in a closed system cannot be changed by interaction of the bodies within the system. Also, the angular momentum of a system remains unchanged by interaction within the system.

F. *Conservation of Movement of the Center of Gravity.* The state of rest or motion of the center of gravity of a system cannot be altered by interaction within the system.

G. *Conservation of Charge.* Whenever a charge Q is generated at one place in a system, an equal and opposite charge $-Q$ must appear elsewhere in the system.

* The conservation laws for mass or energy alone should not be applied in atomic physics or astronomy.

II. Illustration

These conservation laws provide a base from which all physical phenomena may be explained. The conservation of energy law is a particularly powerful tool which relates all types of energy: chemical, mechanical, heat, light, sound, and mass.

An interesting effect is the Coriolis force, which may be deduced from energy conservation. If liquid is flowing into the base of a tube with a configuration of a T and out of both arms, then a torque (proportional to the flow) must be exerted to keep the T in rotation about the axis of its main tube.

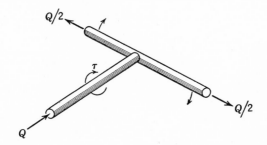

The conservation of momentum is utilized in turbine wheel and jet propulsion design.

III. Magnitude

The units of energy are related as follows:

$$1 \text{ Btu} = 778 \text{ ft-lb}$$

$$1 \text{ lb} = 10^8 \text{ ft-lb} \quad (E = mc^2)$$

IV. References

1. Page, Leigh, *Introduction to Theoretical Physics*, D. Van Nostrand and Co., New York, 1952. Reference for the conservation of dynamical energy, momentum, energy.

Quantities

Charge	Energy (P.E.)	Mass	Sound
Energy (K.E.)	Light	Momentum	Velocity

CONSTANT HEAT CAPACITY LAWS

(Also known as Du Long and Petit's law, atomic heat, and
atomic heat capacity.)

I. Description

The product of the atomic weight and the specific heat for the solid
state has approximately the same value for most elements.

II. Illustration

The law of constant heat capacity is a limiting law, for all solid elements at constant volume tend with increasing temperature towards
the same limiting value of atomic heat. For instance, diamonds at
room temperature have very low atomic heat, but at 900°F the limiting value has almost been reached.

III. Magnitude

This empirical law is approximately true only for solids, the mean
constant being 6.4.

This law holds fairly well for elements with atomic weights greater
than 40. Some of these elements which agree well with this law are:

Copper	5.88
Silver	6.03
Iron	6.12
Gold	6.25
Lead	6.52
Uranium	6.61

The chief variations are the nonmetallic elements with low atomic
weight. Examples are:

Carbon	1.8
Hydrogen	2.3
Boron	2.7

Beryllium	3.7
Silicon	3.8
Oxygen	4.0
Phosphorus	5.4
Sulfur	5.4
Germanium	5.5

The product is also affected by temperature, the value increasing with increasing temperature.

IV. References

1. Richtmyer, F. K., and E. H. Kennard, *Introduction to Modern Physics,* McGraw-Hill Book Co., New York, 1955. A discussion (mathematical and otherwise) of specific heats.
2. Friend, J. Newton, *A Textbook of Physical Chemistry,* Vol. 1, J. B. Lippincott Co., Philadelphia, 1933, pp. 216–221. Violations of the law and some explanation.

Quantities

Chemical composition   Specific heat   Temperature

CORBINO EFFECT

I. Description

If a circular disk that is carrying a current radially is placed at right angles to a magnetic field, a current component is seen to flow around the disk. This is generally considered a special application of the Hall effect (charges moving perpendicular to a magnetic field).

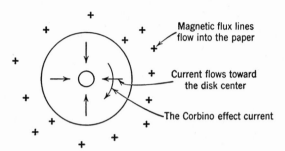

II. Illustration

The Corbino effect decreases for bismuth at higher flux densities. The effect may cause current in either direction, antimony being the reverse of bismuth in its effect. The effect is independent of the thickness of the disk. For iron, nickel, cobalt, bismuth and antimony, the effect is not proportional to the field. This effect has been observed for two electrolytes in contact, that is, poured one on top of the other.

III. Magnitude

This law is expressed mathematically as:

$$C = \frac{cBI}{2} \ln \frac{(r_2)}{(r_1)}$$

where C = circular current in amp

c = Corbino constant in gauss^{-1}

B = magnetic field density in kilogauss

I = total radial current flow in amp

r_1 = inner radius of disk

r_2 = outer radius of disk

For several metals

Material	B	$c \times 10^{-7}$
Copper	2.82	−3.36
	7.31	−2.38
Iron	1.39	+7.45
	8.45	+7.13
Aluminum	7.97	−0.77
Bismuth	0.03	−711.0
	2.63	−613.0
	7.72	−381.0

IV. References

1. Campbell, L. L., *Galvanomagnetic and Thermomagnetic Effects*, Longmans, Green and Co., New York, 1923, pp. 125–137. Relates Hall effect and Corbino effect, details of apparatus, and constants.
2. Washburn, Edward W. (Editor), *International Critical Tables*, Vol. 6, McGraw-Hill Book Co., New York, 1929, pp. 415–419. Diagram and tables constants.
See also Galvanomagnetic and Thermomagnetic Effects.

Quantities

Chemical composition　　　Current　　　Length　　　Magnetic flux

COSMIC RAYS

I. Description

Cosmic rays are highly penetrating radiations which originate outside the earth and consist of photons, electrons, neutrons, protons, and other particles.

Latitude effect

The intensity of cosmic rays is minimum at the equator, maximum at the poles. This variation follows the geomagnetic latitude, but there is essentially no change in intensity for latitudes greater than 50°. The effect is caused by the earth's magnetic field which screens the equatorial regions from all rays having less than 15 Bev (billion electron volts), but for latitudes greater than 50° only 4 Bev are needed. Particles with energy of less than 4 Bev cannot reach the earth because of the influence of the magnetic field of the sun. This change in intensity with latitude is about 10% at sea level and 90% at the top of the atmosphere.

East-West effect

Because of the magnetic field of the earth and the charge of the cosmic rays (positive), more particles approach from the west than from the east.

Altitude effect

The intensity of cosmic rays increases to an altitude of about 50,000 ft, after which it starts to decrease. The incoming rays (hard rays) react with the atmospheric gases producing secondary particles (soft cosmic rays) which first increase the total intensity with decreasing altitude. The absorbing effect of the atmosphere then starts to be important and decreases the total intensity. The variation in altitude from sea level to maximum may be 35 to 1. The intensity of the hard rays increases with increasing altitude.

Showers

Showers are produced by either hard or soft cosmic rays reacting with the matter through which they are passing. First, the incident particle jars loose a number of other particles which in turn release more. The multiplication process continues until the energy level decreases enough so that the radiation is absorbed by the material. Showers are produced by lead, with the thickness for maximum effect for this material 2 cm. Large showers occur in the air. There is about one each hour a thousand feet or more across and about one a week covering an area a mile in diameter.

Bursts

Bursts are a sudden increase in apparent cosmic ray activity caused by showers from the walls or shielding of the detector, or the disintegration of a nucleus close enough to the chamber to send some decomposition products through the detector.

Stars

These are the tracks left by the pieces of a disintegrating nucleus expelling products in several directions. There may be 2 to 10 or more branches, the average number being 3 or 4.

II. Reference

1. Glasstone, Samuel, *Sourcebook on Atomic Energy*, D. Van Nostrand Co., New York, 1950, pp. 475–484. Aspects of cosmic rays and some experiments. Cosmic ray phenomena, pp. 489–496.

Quantities

Angle	Direction	Position
Concentration	Energy (K.E.)	Radiation

===

COULOMB'S LAW

I. Description

The law covers the fields of electrostatics, magnetostatics, and the dynamics of particles; the latter is known as Newton's law of gravitation. The law describes the force of attraction or repulsion between two bodies as inversely proportional to the squared distance between them and proportional to the product of the particular phenomenon involved in each particle, i.e., charge, magnetic pole strength, or mass.

II. Illustration

Coulomb's law can be used as a method for measuring voltage electrostatically. Its advantage is that it requires no current for its operation. One such device uses the voltage to force a charge on two gold leaves that are connected together at the top and separated at the bottom. The sign of the charge on both leaves is the same. The angle the leaves make with each other is a measure of the voltage. The effect is also used in the production of Lichtenberg's figures, or more recently Xerographic printing. The former is used in peak voltage determinations for fault recorders.

III. Magnitude

The electrostatic attraction or repulsion between two charged bodies is proportional to the magnitude of these charges and inversely proportional to the square of the distance between them.

This may be expressed by the equation:

$$F = \frac{Q_1 Q_2}{\epsilon r^2}$$

where F = force in dynes
  ϵ = dielectric constant
  Q = charge in stat-coulombs
  r = distance in cm

This same law applies for two isolated magnetic poles with the strength of the poles used instead of charge, and permeability instead of dielectric constant. Using masses instead of charges, the equation becomes Newton's law of gravitation by substituting

$$\frac{1}{\epsilon} = g = 6.66 \times 10^8 \frac{cm^3}{g\text{-}sec^2}$$

where g = constant of gravitation

Two equal charges, each 10^{-6} coulomb, separated by a distance of 10 cm would produce a force of 9×10^4 dynes of each other if in a vacuum.

Some values of dielectric constant that are usable in the above equation are:

Material	ϵ
Water (pure)	81
Air (0°C and 760 mm)	1.0006
Mica	5.8
Rubber	2.5
Barium and strontium titanates (near Curie temperature)	10,000

IV. References

1. Page, Leigh, *Introduction to Theoretical Physics*, D. Van Nostrand Co., New York, 1952, pp. 371–373. A mathematical treatment.
2. Attwood, Stephen S., *Electric and Magnetic Fields*, John Wiley and Sons, New York, 1949. Coulomb's law for charges and poles, plus relativistic effects on field of moving charge.

Quantities

Charge	Force	Magnetic flux	Permeability
Dielectric constant	Length	Mass	

CURIE-WEISS LAW

I. Description

The Curie-Weiss law states that all ferromagnetic substances have a definite transition temperature at which the phenomenon of ferromagnetism disappears and the substance becomes merely paramagnetic. This temperature is called Curie point and is usually lower than the melting point. (Also ferroelectric substances exhibit a definite change in the dielectric constant at certain temperatures called Curie points.)

The Curie-Weiss law states the susceptibility of the paramagnetic substance above the Curie point varies inversely as the temperature above that point. At or below the Curie point, the Curie-Weiss law does not hold.

The peremeability of certain nickel-base alloys varies with temperature. With increasing temperature this variation may be almost anything, depending on the material.

II. Illustration

The change in permeability of the material with temperature may be used to control the temperature of an area or the inductance of a circuit. Permanent magnetic circuits, such as in electric meters, may be compensated for temperature errors by suitable magnetic shunts.

Since a change in permeability also causes a change in volume, glass to metal seals are made to have the same expansion coefficient by using Fernico or Kovar, whose total expansion coefficient due to both heat and permeability is made the same as the glass to which it is sealed.

III. Magnitude

The following expression is a version of the Curie-Weiss law:

$$I = \frac{AH}{T}$$

where H = magnetic field intensity
I = resultant intensity of magnetization
T = temperature
A = Curie-Weiss constant
(can be used for paramagnetic substances)

With a choice of alloys, the variation of permeability with temperature may be made large—as high as 100:1 for a 50°C change.

The Curie temperature may vary from below 0°C to 800°C. Dysprosium is highly magnetic below 105°K (−168°C).

IV. References

1. Bhatmayer, S. S., and K. N. Mather, *Physical Principles and Applications to Magneto-chemistry,* Macmillan and Co., Ltd., London, 1935, pp. 144–150. Derivation of Curie-Weiss law.

Quantities

Chemical composition   Magnetic flux   Permeability   Temperature

DEBYE FREQUENCY EFFECT

I. Description

The conductance of an electrolyte will increase with the frequency of the applied voltage.

II. Illustration

This effect ties together the frequency of the applied voltage, conductance of the fluid, the volume mobility, and concentration of the ions. This relation is especially true for the weak electrolytes such as acetic acid.

III. Magnitude

Since the equation for the effect is complicated, see reference below for the equations. The magnitude of this effect is less than that found for the Wien effect.

IV. Reference

1. Dole, Malcolm, *Principles of Experimental and Theoretical Electro-Chemistry*, McGraw-Hill Book Co., New York, 1935, pp. 117–118. A brief discussion of the effect with equations.

Quantities

Chemical composition	Current	Resistivity
Concentration	Frequency	

DIFFRACTION

I. Description

The spreading of a beam of energy into the region behind an obstacle is known as diffraction. This applies to all traveling wave phenomena.

II. Illustration

Diffraction gratings employing this principle are used in spectroscopy.

The phenomenon is also used to study crystal lattices by the use of X-rays and is known in this application as the law of crystal diffraction or Bragg's law. By means of this law, either the atomic spacing of the crystal or the wavelength of the X-rays can be determined by experiment if the other one of these quantities is known.

Other examples of diffraction are Fresnel fringes which may be used to determine the diameter of small wires.

III. Magnitude

This phenomenon limits the resolving power of lenses as expressed by the formula:

$$\theta = \frac{1.22\lambda}{D}$$

where θ = limiting angle of resolution
λ = wavelength of the radiation
D = diameter of the lens

Bragg's equation expressing Bragg's law has been derived for X-ray:

$$n\lambda = 2d \sin \phi$$

where n = an integer
d = distance between atomic planes
ϕ = angle of refraction of rays from planes

IV. References

1. Hausmann, E. and E. Slack, *Physics,* D. Van Nostrand Co., New York, 1948, pp. 725–732. A qualitative and quantitative discussion for slits, lenses, gratings, and crystals.
2. Richtmyer, F. R. and E. H. Kennard, *Introduction to Modern Physics,* McGraw-Hill Book Co., New York, 1955. Bragg's equation and uses.
3. Page, Leigh, *Introduction to Theoretical Physics,* D. Van Nostrand Co., New York, 1952, pp. 612–633. Diffraction results theoretically derived for a number of cases.
4. Preston, Thomas A., *The Theory of Light,* Macmillan and Co., Ltd., London, 1929, pp. 242–334. Diffraction lines, how produced; diffraction gratings, calculations, how made; prism, some uses.
5. Sugg, Ronald E., "An Interferometer for Examining Polished Surfaces," *Mechanical Engineering,* Volume 75, No. 8, August, 1953, pp. 629–631. Industrial use of interferometer.

See also Snell's Law, Gladstone and Dale's Law.

Quantities

Angle	Diffraction	Length	Radiation
Color	Frequency	Light	Sound

DOPPLER-FIZEAU EFFECT

I. Description

The wavelength of a disturbance of fixed frequency may be altered if motion is imparted to the source or receiver of the disturbance.

between the equation of a moving source or that of a moving observer. Relativistic equations may at times be necessary for all electromagnetic radiation.

IV. References

1. Richtmyer, F. K., and E. H. Kennard, *Introduction to Modern Physics*, McGraw-Hill Book Co., New York, 1955. Doppler effect on width of spectral lines.
2. Page, Leigh, *Introduction to Theoretical Physics*, D. Van Nostrand Co., New York, 1952, pp. 648–649. Doppler effect on light frequency.
3. Hausmann, E., and E. Slack, *Physics*, D. Van Nostrand Co., New York, 1948, pp. 586–587. Three cases for sound.

Quantities

Frequency	Radiation	Sound
Light	Reflection	Velocity

ELASTIC LIMIT

I. Description

Elastic limit is the maximum stress to which a body may be subjected without causing permanent deformation after the load is relaxed to zero. To assign metals some measure of the elastic limit, a yield strength in pounds per square inch is determined by finding the load that exceeds the elastic limit a small amount and produces a 0.1, 0.5, or 1.0% permanent set in the material.

II. Illustration

This stress limit is the one used in designing structural members.

The elastic limit is used indirectly to determine the hardness of a material. In a Rockwell hardness tester, a conical diamond stylus has its pointed end forced into the surface of a material; and then the force is released. The depth of plastic penetration is used as a measure of surface hardness. A Brinell hardness tester does much the same thing, except a steel ball is used.

Springs stressed above this limit change their properties.

III. Magnitude

Loads of 150 kg are applied to the Rockwell diamond cone and the penetration is only a few thousandths of an inch.

For some common materials, the yield strengths (permanent set of 0.1%) are:

	Yield Strength, psi
Aluminum (cold rolled)	18,700
Cast iron	6,000
Magnesium, drawn, annealed	12,000
Phosphor bronze	59,000
Steel, spring tempered	130,000

IV. References

1. Faires, I. V. M., *Design of Machine Elements,* The Macmillan Co., New York, 1955, Chapter I.
2. Young, J. F., *Materials and Processes,* John Wiley and Sons, New York, 1954, pp. 87–88.

See also Hooke's Law.

Quantities

Chemical composition   Strain   Stress

ELECTROCAPILLARITY

I. Description

The surface tension between two conducting liquids in contact, such as mercury and dilute acid, is sensibly altered when an electric current passes across the interface. As a result, when the contact is in a capillary tube, the pressure difference across the meniscus is affected by a current traversing the capillary column, the amount depending upon the magnitude and direction of the current across this boundary.

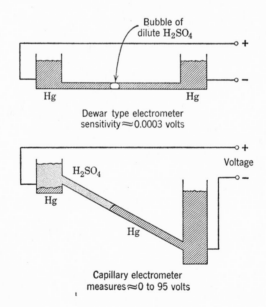

Bubble of
dilute H_2SO_4

Hg   Hg

Dewar type electrometer
sensitivity $\approx$ 0.0003 volts

H_2SO_4

Voltage

Hg

Hg

Capillary electrometer
measures $\approx$ 0 to 95 volts

II. Illustration

This effect has been utilized in different forms of capillary electrometers. In the Dewar type, two small vessels of mercury are joined below the mercury level by a capillary tube, in which the mercury is interrupted by a short space filled with dilute acid. Upon applying a small potential difference to the two bodies of mercury, the equilibrium is disturbed and the drop of acid moves toward the low-potential end until the resultant capillary pressure is balanced by the hydrostatic pressure of the mercury.

III. Magnitude

Since this effect is approximately proportional to the potential difference, the apparatus described above serves as a sensitive indicator for potentials as low as 0.0003 volt.

IV. References

1. Glasstone, S., *Textbook of Physical Chemistry*, D. Van Nostrand Co., New York, 2nd Ed., 1946, p. 1203.
2. Atkinson, E., Translation of *Ganot's Physics*, William Wood and Co., New York, 1910, pp. 992–4. A qualitative description.
3. Dole, Malcolm, *Principles of Experimental and Theoretical Electro-Chemistry*, McGraw-Hill Book Co., New York, 1935, pp. 466–478. Examples, thermodynamics, and theory of the phenomenon.

Quantities

Current	Force	Pressure
Flow	Potential	Surface tension

ELECTROKINETIC PHENOMENA

I. Description

Electro-osmosis (electroendosmosis) is the movement of a polar fluid or an electrolyte by an electric current through a porous diaphragm. The converse is also true. The movement of a liquid through a porous diaphragm induces a voltage (streaming potential) across the diaphragm proportional to the pressure difference.

Cataphoresis is essentially the same phenomenon as electro-osmosis. Instead of a fluid passing through a small capillary, suspended colloids, acting as the capillary walls, move in a direction reverse to that of the fluid. This effect does not exist for higher voltages. The inverse of cataphoresis is also true; particles settling produce an emf. The effect is very sensitive to particle composition.

II. Illustration

The principle may be used as a flow meter or as a transducer.

The phenomenon is used to drain water from and thus stiffen walls of excavations in mud and clay.

III. Magnitude

The electro-osmostic pressure developed for a number of fluids is proportional to the dielectric constant of the fluid:

$$\frac{P}{P_0} = \frac{K - K_g}{K_0 - K_g}$$

where P = pressure of fluid
  P_0 = pressure of reference fluid
  K = dielectric constant of fluid
  K_0 = dielectric constant of reference fluid
  K_g = dielectric constant of tube (often glass)

The directions for the streaming current and fluid flow are the same, at least for water. The sensitivity may be 250 to 500 millivolts per psi. The voltage is affected by the concentration of the electrolyte, but is a linear function of pressure differences. This effect is used in the Cottrell precipitator (for dusts) as well as in the electrodeposition of materials such as rubber.

For cataphoresis, some particle velocities are:

Dispersed Material	Particle Size	Velocity per 1 volt/cm
Quartz	1μ	3×10^{-4} cm/sec
Gold	Below $100\mu\mu$	2.2
Platinum	Below $100\mu\mu$	2.0
Ferric oxide	Below $100\mu\mu$	3.0
Silver	Below $100\mu\mu$	2.4
Iron	Below $100\mu\mu$	1.9
Oil (emulsion)	About 2μ	3.2
Air bubbles	About 0.1 mm	4

IV. References

1. E. Atkinson's translation of *Ganot's Physics*, William Wood and Co., New York, 1910, pp. 944–5. A qualitative discussion.
2. Hartway, Jr., E. V., "Electrokinetic Transducers," *Instruments*, August, 1953, Vol. 26, No. 8, pp. 1186–88. History, theory, application.
3. MacDougall, Frank H., *Physical Chemistry*, The Macmillan Co., New York, 1952, pp. 455–462. Mechanisms of transference with numbers, pp. 716–723. Electrokinetic phenomena. Explanation and mathematics.
4. Dole, Malcolm, *Principles of Experimental and Theoretical Electro-Chemistry*, McGraw-Hill Book Co., New York, 1935, pp. 443–465. Electrokinetic phenomena, history, explanation, and some uses.
5. Loughney, R., "Electricity Stiffens Clay Fireball for Electric Plant Excavation," *Construction Methods and Equipment*, Vol. 36, No. 8, August, 1954, p. 70.

Quantities

Chemical composition	Direction	Potential
Current	Flow	Pressure

EOTVOS EFFECT

I. Description

A postulate of Galileo-Newtonian mechanics is that a body moving east decreases in weight but increases in weight when going west.

This effect should be taken into account when measuring the force of gravity on the earth's surface.

This is a special example of the Coriolis effect, though complicated by gravity.

II. Illustration

A pendulum on the surface of the earth will swing with a motion which is not exactly harmonic in the E-W direction, but its motion will be harmonic in a N-S direction.

III. Magnitude

The magnitude of the gravitational acceleration is

$$g = g_0 - 2\Omega \cos \phi \frac{dy}{dt}$$

where g = effective gravity
g_0 = gravitational acceleration
Ω = angular velocity of the earth
ϕ = geographical latitude

$\frac{dy}{dt}$ = velocity in rectangular coordinates with axes N and E

IV. References

1. Gray, Andrew, *A Treatise on Gyrostatics and Rotational Motion*, Macmillan and Co., Ltd., 1918, London, pp. 523-4. The mathematical outline.

2. *Science Abstracts,* Section A, Vol. 23, 1920. Abstract No. 26, p. 8. Abstract of article by Eotvos giving formula.

Quantities

| Direction | Mass | Position | Velocity |

EXPANSION / TEMPERATURE OR THERMAL EXPANSION

I. Description

The coefficient of linear expansion or expansivity is the ratio of the change in length per degree C to the length at 0°C. The coefficient of volume expansion (for solids) is approximately three times the linear coefficient. The coefficient of volume expansion for liquids is the ratio of the change in volume per degree to the volume at 0°C. The value of the coefficient varies with temperature. The coefficient of volume expansion for a gas under constant pressure is nearly the same for all gases and temperatures and is equal to 0.00367 for 1°C.

II. Illustration

The mercury thermometer is a good example of this effect. A glass bulb containing a quantity of mercury is connected to a fine glass tube. A change in temperature varies the volume of the mercury, and these small changes in volume show up as large variations of the length of mercury in the thin tube.

By the joining of two different metals, bimetal, differential expansion is used to obtain relatively large dimensional movements.

III. Magnitude

Expansion/temperature may be broken up into the expansion of solids, liquids, and gases.

A. *Expansion of solids vs. temperature*

Solids expand linearly with temperature. The equation for this expansion in one direction is:

$$L_T = L_0(1 + \alpha T)$$

where L_T = length at temperature T (meters)

L_0 = length at 0°C (meters)

α = temperature coefficient of expansion (meters/meter − °C);
(may be negative as for stretched rubber and silver iodide)

T = temperature (°C)

At very low temperatures $\alpha \to 0$ for some materials.

Example. Mercury has a linear expansion coefficient of 0.000030/°C. Steel has a linear coefficient of expansion of 0.000011 to 0.000015/°C.

B. *Expansion of liquids vs. temperature*

Liquids do not expand linearly with temperature. Their expansion is one hundred or more times that of a solid. The equation for the volumetric expansion of liquids is as follows:

$$V_T = V_0(1 + aT + bT^2 + cT^3 \ldots)$$

where V_T = volume at temperature T (cu ft)

V_0 = volume at 0°C (cu ft)

a = coefficient of expansion (cu ft/cu ft − °C)

b = coefficient of expansion (cu ft/cu ft − °C^2)

c = coefficient of expansion (cu ft/cu ft − °C^3)

T = temperature (°C)

Examples. Mercury has a cubical expansion coefficient of:

$$a = 0.181 \times 10^{-3}$$

$$b = 0.0076 \times 10^{-6}$$

Water has a cubical expansion coefficient of:

$$a = -6.43 \times 10^{-5}$$

$$b = 8.50 \times 10^{-6}$$

$$c = 6.79 \times 10^{-8}$$

C. Expansion of gases vs. temperature

Gases expand five or ten times more than most liquids. Most gases have nearly the same coefficient of expansion. This coefficient is 1/273.18 of the gas volume per °C for an ideal gas assuming constant pressure. An ideal gas is defined as one which obeys Boyle's law exactly and has a constant coefficient of expansion. The equation for the volumetric expansion of an ideal gas, assuming that pressure is constant, is as follows:

$$V_T = V_0(1 + aT)$$

where V_T = volume at temperature T (cu ft)
V_0 = volume at °C (cu ft)
a = temperature coefficient (1/273.18 cu ft/cu ft − °C)
T = temperature (°C)

IV. References

1. Hodgman, C. D., *Handbook of Chemistry and Physics,* Chemical Rubber Publishing Co., Cleveland, 1955. Tables of coefficients and equations.
2. Hausmann, E., and E. Slack, *Physics,* D. Van Nostrand Co., New York, 1948, Chapter XIV. General discussion.

Quantities

Coefficient of expansion   Length   Temperature   Volume

FARADAY EFFECT (MAGNETO-OPTICAL ROTATION)

I. Description

When a magnetic field is applied to a transparent material through which plane polarized light is passed, there will be a rotation of the plane of polarization. This rotation, called the Faraday effect, is proportional to the length of material in the magnetic field, the strength of the magnetic field, the cosine of the angle between the magnetic field and the ray of light, and Verdet's constant.

The Verdet's constant is a function of temperature, the type of material, and is approximately proportional to the square of the frequency of the light. The rotation decreases with an increase in temperature. There is a time lag before this rotation after the application of the field.

II. Illustration

This effect could be used to detect the strength of an alternating magnetic field. Reflecting the beam back through the field and material doubles the effect in activated vapors. The specific rotation for many materials is little affected by the concentration of the solution.

III. Magnitude

This effect may be expressed by the equation:

$$\theta = VLB \cos \phi \left(\frac{n^2}{\lambda}\right)\left(n - \lambda \frac{dn}{d\lambda}\right)$$

where θ = angular rotation of plane of polarization in minutes of arc.
V = Verdet's constant
L = length in centimeters of material in the field
B = magnetic field intensity in gauss

ϕ = angle between H and direction of the light
n = index of refraction of the material
λ = wavelength of light in free space

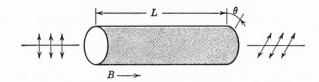

Verdet's constant for water at the sodium D line is approximately 0.013′/cm gauss. For glass (very heavy flint) V goes up to 0.09′/cm gauss for D line, both values for 20°C.

Temperature effect may be illustrated with water for which V = 0.0131 at 0°C and V = 0.0127 at 100°C.

Using 7 cm of very heavy flint glass, it would require a field of 100 gauss to give an angular rotation of 1°.

IV. References

1. Jenkins, F. A., and H. E. White, *Fundamentals of Physical Optics,* McGraw-Hill Book Co., New York, 1950. Shows relation to Zeeman effect.
2. Bhatmayer, S. S., and K. N. Mathur, *Physical Principles and Applications of Magneto-chemistry,* Macmillan and Co., Ltd., London, 1935, pp. 251–271. Extensive discussion of many experiments with theory.
See also Zeeman Effect.

Quantities

Angle	Frequency	Length	Magnetic flux	Temperature
Chemical composition	Index of refraction	Light	Polarization	

FARADAY'S LAW OF ELECTROLYSIS

I. Description

A. *First Law*. Whenever an electric current passes across a junction between a purely metallic and a purely electrolytic conductor, a chemical change occurs, which amount, expressed in chemical equivalents, is exactly proportional to the quantity of electricity which passes. The chemical equivalent weight is the amount of a substance liberated by a unit current for unit time.

B. *Second Law*. In electrolysis the quantities of the different substances which separate at the electrodes throughout the circuit are directly proportional to their chemical equivalent weights. They are independent of the concentration and the temperature of the solution, the size of the electrodes, and all other circumstances. The voltage developed across the cell will vary with the concentration of the electrolyte and current. The chemical equivalent weight of an element is the ratio of its atomic weight in grams to its valence number.

II. Illustration

In electrolysis of many metallic salts, other than those of the alkali and alkaline earth metals, the metal is deposited at the cathode or negative junction between a metallic and an electrolytic conductor. Copper or lead is refined or deposited on another metal or graphite by electric deposition; nickel, silver, gold, zinc, cadmium, or chromium are deposited in electroplating on objects. Sodium and potassium may be electrolyzed through glass. For potassium this requires a lead and sodium free glass.

III. Magnitude

96,500 coulombs of electricity will deposit 107.88 grams of silver or 31.8 grams of copper.

IV. References

1. Hausmann, E., and E. Slack, *Physics,* D. Van Nostrand Co., New York, 1948, pp. 401–404. Discussion and sample calculations. Mechanism of electrolysis, pp. 398–401.
2. Hodgman, Charles D., *Handbook of Chemistry and Physics,* Chemical Rubber Publishing Co., Cleveland, Ohio, 1955. Electrochemical equivalents of the elements.
3. Dole, Malcolm, *Principles of Experimental and Theoretical Electro-Chemistry,* McGraw-Hill Book Co., New York, 1935, pp. 30–38. Electrolysis discussion.

Quantities

Chemical	Current	Molecular	Potential
composition	Energy (P.E.)	weight	Resistivity
Concentration	Mass		

====================

FARADAY'S LAW OF INDUCTION

I. Description

If, for any reason, the number of lines of flux which thread through a conductor is altered, an electromotive force will be produced in the conductor during the change.

II. Illustration

The emf is induced in the circuit regardless of the cause of the flux variation. The flux may change in magnitude or direction to produce a variation, or a conductor in the circuit may move through the lines of flux. The most common application of this law applies to rotating coils or windings having an emf induced as they cut through a magnetic field. If A is the area enclosed by each coil, N is the number of coils, B is the magnetic flux density perpendicular to the axis of rotation, and ω is the angular velocity; then the peak value of induced emf is:

$$V = NBA\omega$$

Lenz's law illustrates this equation. When an electrical conductor forming a closed circuit or part of a closed circuit is moved in a magnetic field in such a way that a change takes place in the number of lines of magnetic induction passing through the circuit, a current is induced in the circuit and the mechanical force set up is such that this force tends to stop the motion which gave rise to the current.

Every action on a system, which in producing a change in its state involves a transformation of energy, sets up reactions tending to preserve unchanged the configuration of the system. Similarly when a conductor is moved in the presence of a magnet, induction comes into play and an emf is set up between various parts of the block and causes currents of electricity to flow within it. These are known as eddy or Foucault currents.

The eddy current loss (Foucault current) in a core is the result of currents induced in the core by the varying magnetic flux. The magnitude of the power loss per unit volume is proportional to the square of the frequency, to the square of the flux density, inversely proportional to the resistivity of the core material, and directly proportional to the square of the thickness (or diameter) of the individual core laminations (or particles).

III. Magnitude

The line integral of the total electric field strength, E, or intensity taken around any closed path, of length l, is proportional to the negative rate of change with respect to time of the magnetic flux, B, across any surface bounded by that path, a:

$$\oint E dl = \frac{-dB}{dt} \cdot da$$

The common expression for an induced emf in any circuit is proportional to the rate of change of the magnetic flux enclosed by the circuit:

$$E = -10^{-8}N\frac{d\phi}{dt}$$

where E = volts

N = number of turns of the coil

ϕ = magnetic flux in maxwells enclosed by the coil

t = time in sec

At Cambridge, Mass., the magnitude of the earth's field is 0.58 gauss or 5800 maxwells/square meter. If a single coil enclosing an area of one square meter was rotated at 3600 rpm at this location, it could generate a peak emf of 0.007 volt (on the strength of the earth's field alone).

IV. References

1. Page, Leigh, *Introduction to Theoretical Physics,* D. Van Nostrand Co., New York, 1952, pp. 472–475. A mathematical treatment.
2. Cohn, George I., "Electromagnetic Induction," *Electrical Engineering,* Vol. 68, May, 1949, American Institute of Electrical Engineers, New York, pp. 441–447. An extensive evaluation of the applications of and exceptions to the various common formulas.
3. Skilling, H. H., *Fundamentals of Electric Waves,* John Wiley and Sons, New York, 2nd Ed., 1948, Chapter 6. Complete discussion of derivation.

Quantities

Current	Inductance	Magnetic flux	Time
Energy (P.E.)	Length	Potential	Velocity

FERRANTI EFFECT

I. Description

There are lengths of transmission lines and frequencies of transmitted electrical waves for which the line load voltage may be greater than the sending end voltage.

The voltage gain by such an effect is limited only by the constants of the lines involved and the open circuit conditions. The effect is frequency sensitive as might be expected since impedance is a function of frequency.

II. Illustration

The Ferranti effect can be illustrated by calculation from the equation shown under magnitude on a 165-mil diameter copper wire line

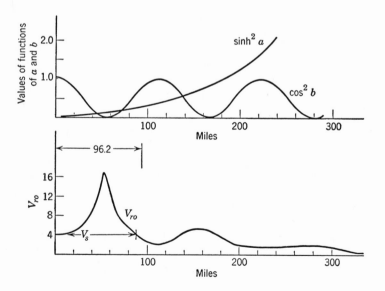

with 12 inch spacing between the wires having the following parameters per loop mile:

$R = 4.02$ ohms $\qquad C = 0.00898$ μf between wires

$L = 3.37$ mh $\qquad G = 5$ μmhos

at 796 cycles per second (wavelength—228.5 miles)

$$\alpha = 0.0048 \text{ neper/mile}$$

$$\beta = 0.0275 \text{ radius/mile}$$

V_{r0}, $\sinh^2 a$, and $\cos^2 b$ are plotted on the previous page.

III. Magnitude

An expression can be derived which will give the open circuit end voltage of a transmission line wherein I_r (receiving end current) $= 0$. One such expression is:

$$V_{r0} = \frac{V_s \;/ -\tan^{-1}(\tan b \tanh a)}{\sqrt{\sinh^2 a + \cos^2 b}}$$

where $\quad V_{r0} =$ receiving end voltage

$V_s =$ sending end voltage

$S\sqrt{ZY} = a + jb = S(\alpha + j\beta)$

$S =$ line length

$Z =$ unit series impedance of the line

$Y =$ unit shunt admittance of the line

Examining the equation, it can be seen that when $\sinh^2 a + \cos^2 b = 1$, V_{r0} is greater that V_s. As the line length increases $\sinh^2 a$ increases from zero to ever higher values. At the same time $\cos^2 b$ decreases from 1 to 0 and back to 1, etc. Thus, for certain relatively short lines this effect is observed. This must be before $\sinh^2 a = 1$ because the lowest value $\cos^2 b$ can have is zero.

IV. Reference

1. Ware, L. A., and H. R. Reed, *Communication Circuits,* John Wiley and Sons, New York, 3rd Ed., 1949.

Quantities

Capacitance	Inductance	Potential
Frequency	Length	Resistivity

FERROELECTRIC PHENOMENA

I. Description

Some dielectrics exhibit nonlinear and hysteresis effects in the relationship between applied voltage and field strength in the material. These dielectrics are said to be a ferroelectric material. Such materials have microscopic domains, each polarized in the absence of an applied field. Most ferroelectric materials are also electrostrictive. Some ferroelectric materials are in addition piezoelectric.

The ferroelectric Curie temperature is the upper temperature limit of this ferroelectric property for a given material. Changes also appear in the latent heat and specific heat of a sample at this temperature.

II. Illustration

Some materials exhibiting these phenomena are:

Rochelle salt (as well as ammonium and lithium tantalum tartrates). (Curie temperature $-18°$ to $23°C$)

Potassium dihydrophosphate (KH_2PO_4) (as well as the dihydrogen phosphates and arsenates of the alkali metals). (Curie temperatures $123°K$ to $213°K$.)

Barium titanate (other similar ones are $KTaO_3$, $NaTaO_3$, $KNbO_3$, and $NaNbO_3$). (Curie temperatures $120°C$ to $913°K$.)

These materials have been used in dielectric amplifiers operating in manner analogous to magnetic amplifiers.

III. Magnitude

Capacitor dielectrics, primarily of the barium titanate family, may have dielectric constants of 3000; this dielectric constant is temperature sensitive and peaks near the Curie temperature, as shown by the Curie-Weiss law:

$$\epsilon = \frac{1.7 \times 10^5}{T - 393}$$

where T is in degrees Kelvin

IV. References

1. Dekker, Adrianus J., *Solid State Physics,* Prentice-Hall, Englewood Cliffs, New Jersey, 1957, pp. 184–209. Excellent readable discussion of theory. No applications.
2. Shirane, G., F. Jona, and R. Pepinsky, "Some Aspects of Ferroelectricity," *Proceedings of the I.R.E.,* December, 1955, p. 1738.
See also Piezoelectric Effect.

Quantities

Capacitance	Dielectric	Electric flux	Potential
Charge	constant	Polarization	Temperature

FICK'S LAWS

I. Description

If two different gases or liquids are allowed to remain in contact, there will be a gradual mixing of the two, even in the absence of convection currents. This mass transfer is due entirely to processes taking place on the scale of atomic or molecular dimensions. Of equal importance is the fact that the same sort of mixing will take place in the solid state, although at a much slower rate. These processes of mixing are called diffusion and are described by Fick's laws. This diffusion takes place moving from an area of more concentration to an area of less concentration at a rate proportional to the concentration gradient. The diffusion may be decreased by the application of a potential between the regions of different concentrations.

II. Illustration

A. When two liquids are carefully poured one on top of the other, they will diffuse according to the expression below.

B. Two metals in contact will also diffuse according to the expression listed below.

III. Magnitude

A. Fick's first law is:

$$P = \frac{dm}{dt} = -DS\frac{dc}{dx}$$

where P = rate of permeation

$\dfrac{dm}{dt}$ = mass of solute diffused per unit time

S = cross-sectional area

$\dfrac{dc}{dx}$ = concentration gradient perpendicular to cross section

D = diffusion coefficient for solute and solution at a given temperature. For any one pair of substances, D is directly proportional to the absolute temperature and is not independent of the concentration for concentrated solutions.

$$D = 0.312 \text{ cm}^2/\text{day for cane sugar}$$

$$D = \frac{RT}{W}$$

where R = gas constant
  T = temperature (absolute)
  W = frictional resistance

B. Fick's second law is derived from the first law considering a nonstationary state of flow. The expression is:

$$\frac{\partial c}{\partial t} = DS\frac{\partial^2 c}{\partial x^2}$$

where $\dfrac{\partial c}{\partial t}$ = change in concentration with time

$\dfrac{\partial^2 c}{\partial x^2}$ = change in concentration gradient with the dimension x.

IV. References

1. Dole, Malcolm, *Principles of Experimental and Theoretical Electro-Chemistry*, McGraw-Hill Book Co., New York, 1935, pp. 137–148. Effect of an Electric Current on Diffusion.
2. Eggert, John, *Physical Chemistry* (translated by S. J. Gregg), Constable and Co., Ltd., London, 1932, pp. 251–3. Fick's Law and Some Derivation.
3. Jost, W., *Diffusion in Solids, Liquids, Gases*, Academic Press, New York, 1952, pp. 1–5. Derivations.
4. Barren, Richard, *Diffusion in and Through Solids*, Cambridge University Press, 1951, pp. 1–5. Derivations.

See also Graham's Law.

Quantities

Area	Concentration	Potential	Time
Chemical composition	Liquid	Temperature	

FISSION

I. Description

Fission is the term used to describe a high energy transmutation process in which a nucleus breaks into two nuclei of approximately equal size as well as emitting particles or radiation.

II. Illustration

Fission is usually induced by bombarding the nucleus with neutrons, protons, deutrons, or gamma rays. The products of fission are not fixed, as uranium 235 may produce about 60 elements whose mass numbers vary from 72 to 150. While heavier elements seem to possess somewhat less stable nuclei, high energy particles have induced fission in some lighter elements such as bismuth, platinum, lead, thallium, and tantalum. At least some of the fission products are radioactive.

III. Magnitude

Because fission liberates a relatively large amount of energy, the process is rather useful. In the fission of a uranium atom, about 200 million electron volts are released, or the fission of 1 gram of uranium per day releases energy at a rate of 1 megawatt. This corresponds to the converting of about 0.1% of the mass into energy.

IV. References

1. Glasstone, Samuel, *Sourcebook on Atomic Energy,* D. Van Nostrand Co., New York, 1950, pp. 258–9 definition, pp. 344–409 history, mechanism uses.
2. Kaplan, I., *Nuclear Physics,* Addison-Wesley Publishing Co., Cambridge, Mass., 1956, Chapter 19. History plus theory.
3. Stephenson, R., *Introduction to Nuclear Engineering,* McGraw-Hill Book Co., New York, 1954, Chapter 2. Engineering applications.

See also Group Displacement Law, Radioactivity.

Quantities

Emissivity   Energy (P.E.)   Energy (K.E.)   Radiation

FLUID FLOW EFFECTS

(A summary)

I. Description

Bernoulli's theorem (see also Bernoulli's theorem as a separate entry)

At any point along a tube through which a fluid is flowing, the sum of the pressure plus the potential energy due to position plus the kinetic energy remain constant (friction being disregarded).

$$H = h + \frac{p}{W} + \frac{v^2}{2g}$$

where H = total head (ft)
  h = elevation (ft)
  p = static pressure (lb/ft^2)
  W = specific weight (lb/ft^3)
  v = velocity (ft/sec)
  g = 32.2 ft/sec^2

Stokes's law (see also Stokes's law as a separate entry)

The ultimate velocity of a small sphere falling under the influence of gravity through a fluid may be derived as:

$$V = \frac{2r^2}{9\mu} (W_1 - W_2)$$

where V = velocity (ft/sec)
  r = radius (ft)
  μ = viscosity of medium (lb-sec/ft^2)
  W_1 = specific weight of sphere (lb/ft^3)
  W_2 = specific weight of fluid

Reynold's number

The friction between a moving fluid and a solid surface is a function of the viscosity and inertia of the fluid. Reynold's number (inertia divided by viscosity) also defines the region of transition from smooth to turbulent flow.

$$N_R = \frac{Vdp}{\mu}$$

where N_R = Reynold's number
V = velocity (ft/sec)
d = diameter or width (ft)
p = density (lb sec^2/ft^4)
μ = viscosity (lb sec/ft^2)

Mach number

As the relative velocities of a fluid and a solid body approach the speed of sound (mach 1), compression shock waves are developed. Abrupt increases in fluid pressure, temperature, density, and entropy occur in the thin area of the shock wave. The drag on the solid body increases sharply near mach 1 and the shape of the leading edge becomes more important than the shape of the trailing edge.

$$N_M = \frac{V}{c}$$

where N_M = mach number
V = relative velocity of solid and fluid (ft/sec)
c = velocity of sound in fluid (ft/sec)

Stability law

Acceleration of fluid flow is an efficient and stable fluid process. Deceleration of fluid flow is an inefficient and unstable process resulting in eddy currents and large energy losses.

Hydraulic jump

The flow of high velocity liquid into a region of low liquid velocity may result in a sudden rise in the level of the liquid. The change in level is proportional to the change in velocity.

Cavitation (see also Cavitation as a separate entry)

If a pressure change occurs in a liquid so that the local pressure is below the vapor pressure, a bubble of vapor is formed. The formation of this bubble or cavity and its subsequent collapse produce high transient pressures and temperatures.

II. Illustration

The Bernoulli theorem is the conservation of energy law applied to fluid mechanics. Such diverse effects as flow measurement in a venturi and the lift of an airfoil may be predicted by this relationship between elevation, pressure, and velocity head.

Stokes's law is applied most accurately to particles of fog, pigment, fly ash, bacteria, pollen, etc. (1 to 100 microns). One of the assumptions in the derivation of Stokes's law is that the velocity of the sphere is so small that none of the resistance to motion is due to the inertia of the fluid. Millikan's oil drop experiment which measured the charge of the electron was based on Stokes's law.

Reynold's number has been empirically related to pressure drop and surface heat transfer. The behavior of fluids ranging from air to molasses flowing in anything from a capillary tube to an aqueduct at any velocity which does not approach sonic speeds may be defined by the appropriate Reynold's number.

Mach numbers approaching and surpassing mach 1 are encountered in the motions of projectiles, high speed aircraft, turbine wheels, propeller tips, and high speed flow of gases. A pointed nose or sharp leading edge results in the least drag at these speeds.

The Stability law may be observed in the smooth lines of a fluid as it approaches and accelerates to pass through a restriction. Just behind the restriction the fluid decelerates with turbulent and eddying lines of flow. A diffuser cone is often placed behind the restriction to minimize eddy current losses.

The hydraulic jump is sometimes used deliberately in order to convert the kinetic energy of the liquid and thus prevent erosion of the channel by high velocity flow.

Cavitation is a destructive phenomenon which causes rapid pitting of turbines, pumps, ship propellers, nozzles. Cavitation is reduced or prevented by the use of smoother surface curvatures and higher fluid pressures.

III. References

1. Weissler, Alfred, "Sono-chemistry: The Production of Chemical Changes with Sound Waves," *The Journal of the Acoustical Society of America*, Vol. 25, No. 4, July, 1953, pp. 651–657. A good survey, mainly concerned with chemical reactions.

2. Willard, G. W., "Ultrasonically Induced Cavitation in Water: A Step by Step Process," *The Journal of the Acoustical Society of America*, Vol. 25, No. 4, July, 1953, pp. 669–686. Qualitative discussion.

3. Hausmann, E., and E. Slack, *Physics,* D. Van Nostrand Co., New

York, 3rd ed., 1948, pp. 216–217. Derivation, statement, and use.

4. Page, Leigh, *Introduction to Theoretical Physics,* D. Van Nostrand Co., New York, 3rd Ed., 1952, pp. 241–243. Derivation and mathematics of Bernoulli's theorem for an incompressible liquid in steady flow.

Quantities

Density	Length	Specific gravity	Vapor pressure
Energy (K.E.)	Mass	Temperature	Velocity
Flow	Pressure	Transmission	Viscosity
		(speed of sound)	

FRICTION EFFECTS

I. Description

Coulomb (dry) friction and wet friction

Coulomb (dry) friction is the resistance that is encountered when two solid surfaces slide or tend to slide over each other. The Coulomb friction refers to surfaces in contact without any contaminating fluids.

Wet friction or lubrication refers to conditions where the surfaces are separated by a thin film. In this case, layers of the lubricant slide over each other with much less effort than dry surfaces.

In general, these types of friction exhibit the following characteristics:

1. The magnitude of the contact area does not influence the friction force.

2. The friction force is proportional to the normal force at the contact surface.

3. Friction is increased between two bodies remaining in contact for some time.

4. Friction is less between surfaces of different kinds of matter than between those of the same kind.

5. Friction is greater at the first movement (static) between surfaces than when the surfaces are in motion (sliding).

Rolling friction

Rolling friction is the resistance to rolling motion of wheels, rollers, balls, etc., when moving loads.

Newton's law of friction (viscosity)

The frictional shearing stress in any gas or liquid is proportional to the viscosity of the fluid and the velocity gradient in the fluid. This law is directly similar to Young's law (Young's modulus), where the shearing stress is proportional to the Young's modulus and the strain.

Stokes's law of friction

The forces which oppose the deformation of a fluid are proportional to the rate of change of strain and the viscosity. This law is very similar to Hooke's law for elastic bodies, for in Hooke's law the force which opposes the deformation of the body is proportional to the modulus of elasticity and the body strain.

II. Illustration

Dry friction is seen acting between the brake shoes and the rim of a wheel, in the grinding stone and the worked metal, and in a house and the piers of its foundations.

Dry friction increases with time. With metal on metal, the increase is almost instantaneous, but with wood on metal, the friction increases for several days. With wood on wood, the static friction will increase for several hours. A lubricant will protract this effect. Dry friction between brass and brass is higher than brass on steel. In this connection, it has been a general rule never to design with two sliding surfaces of the same hardness in contact. Rolling is often substituted for sliding friction, as is the case for wheels when a load is being moved. This frictional resistance is substantially smaller than sliding friction.

Most theoretical investigations in fluid dynamics are based on the concept of a frictionless, incompressible perfect fluid. In the motion of such a perfect fluid, two contacting layers experience no tangential forces (shear stresses), but act on each other only with normal forces; it then follows that fluids offer no internal resistance to changes in shape. The theory relating to perfect fluid is very far developed and accounts for real motions like surface waves and the formation of liquid jets. However, the perfect fluid theory fails completely to account for the drag of a body (d'Alembert's paradox). This unacceptable result of the perfect fluid theory is traced to the fact that inner layers of fluid transmit tangential as well as normal stresses. This is also the case near solid walls wetted by a fluid. These tangential or friction forces in a real fluid are connected with a property of the fluid called viscosity.

III. Magnitude

The expression for Coulomb (dry) friction and for empirical values of wet friction provides the definition for coefficient of friction; it is the ratio of the maximum force of friction between two bodies to the normal force pressing the surfaces together.

Thus:

$$\mu_s = \frac{f_s}{N}$$

where μ_s = coefficient of static or sliding friction

$\quad f_s$ = force of friction

$\quad N$ = normal force

Table I. COEFFICIENTS OF STATIC AND SLIDING FRICTION

| | μ | |
Rubbing Surfaces	Static	Sliding
Bronze on iron	0.19	0.18
Metal on oak	0.62	0.55
Tires on dry pavement	0.90	0.85
Tires on wet pavement	0.74	0.69

The coefficient of rolling friction is:

$$\mu_r = \frac{f_r}{N}$$

where μ_r = coefficient of rolling friction
  f_r = force of rolling friction
  N = normal force

Pneumatic tires on smooth roads have an $\mu_r = 0.02$ to 0.03.

Frictional shear stress is expressed, as Newton's law of friction, thus:

$$T = \nu \frac{du}{dy}$$

where T = friction shear stress
  ν = viscosity

$\dfrac{du}{dy}$ = velocity gradient

Table II. VISCOSITIES OF FLUIDS IN CENTIPOISE

Fluid		ν
Water	@ 32°F	1.308
Air	@ 32°F	0.017
Gasoline	@ 32°F	0.50
Oil SAE 10	@ 60°F	100.0
Heavy crude oil	@ 60°F	3500.0

IV. References

1. Marks, L. S., *Mechanical Engineers' Handbook,* McGraw-Hill Book Co., New York, 5th Ed., 1951. Tables of coefficients of friction.
2. Hausmann, E., and E. Slack, *Physics,* D. Van Nostrand Co., New York, 1948, pp. 86–91. A general discussion of dry and wet friction.
3. Schlichting, Dr. H., *Boundary Layer Theory,* McGraw-Hill Book Co., New York, 1955, pp. 5–9 and pp. 38–46. A qualitative and quantitative description and derivation of Newton's law and Stokes's law.

Quantities

Force	Strain	Velocity
Friction	Stress	Viscosity

GALVANOMAGNETIC AND THERMOMAGNETIC
EFFECTS

(Hall, Ettingshausen, Nernst, and Righi-Leduc Effects)

If upon a thin, flat conducting plate of width b, thickness d, carrying a uniform constant longitudinal current (total current $= I$) of either electricity or heat, there is imposed normally a magnetic field of intensity H, two transverse and two longitudinal effects are set up for either heat or electricity.

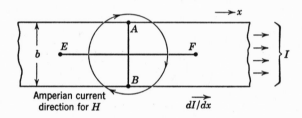

In the absence of a magnetic field, AB is an equipotential or isothermal line.

HALL EFFECT

I. Description

When a current is flowing in a magnetic field, a voltage is developed at right angles to both the magnetic field and the current, and is proportional to the product of the intensity of the current, the magnetic flux and the sine of the angle between the current and the field. When either or both of the quantities mentioned above are varying, the instantaneous voltage would be proportional to the instantaneous values of the current and magnetic field. Near absolute zero a related photomagnetic effect is discernible. (See Photomagnetic Effects.)

II. Illustration

Measurement of the small output of a thermocouple is facilitated with this effect. An alternating magnetic field is applied and an alternating voltage appears between A and B whose magnitude depends on the magnitude of I, and whose phase depends upon the direction of I. This a-c signal may be easily amplified. This effect is also used to measure changes in a magnetic field.

III. Magnitude

The expression for the Hall effect in terms of the Hall effect coefficient, R, (function of materials and temperature) is:

$$E_A - E_B = \frac{RHI}{d}$$

where E_A = potential at A
  E_B = potential at B
  I = current
  H = magnetic field intensity
  d = thickness of the material, parallel to H

For example: The Hall effect coefficients in some materials are:
(a) Bismuth

  $R = 6.9 \times 10^{-8}$ volt $-$ cm/amp gauss at 15 degrees, °C
  $R = 2.5 \times 10^{-8}$ volt $-$ cm/amp gauss at 90 degrees, °C

(b) Tellurium

  $R = 60.0 \times 10^{-8}$ volt $-$ cm/amp gauss at 15 degrees, °C

(c) Germanium

  $R = 8 \times 10^{-5}$ volt $-$ cm/amp gauss at 25 degrees, °C
  R varies at a rate of $-0.1\%/°C$
  Resistivity = 5.7 ohm $-$ cm at 25 degrees, °C

See also Corbino Effect.

ETTINGSHAUSEN EFFECT (VON ETTINGSHAUSEN)

I. Description

When an electric current flows across the lines of force of a magnetic field, an electromotive force is observed which is at right angles to both the primary current and the magnetic field; a temperature gradient is observed which has the opposite direction to the Hall electromotive force.

II. Illustration

The temperature difference between A and B can be used as a measure of the current flowing in the material.

III. Magnitude

The expression for the Ettingshausen effect in terms of the Ettingshausen coefficient, P, is:

$$T_A - T_B = \frac{PHI}{d}$$

where T_A = temperature at A
$\quad T_B$ = temperature at B
$\quad H$ = magnetic field intensity
$\quad I$ = electric current
$\quad d$ = thickness of material parallel to H

P is a function of material and probably of temperature. (This would require further investigation.)

For tellurium P has a value of 3×10^{-4} C/amp meter.

SUPPLEMENTARY GALVANOMAGNETIC EFFECTS

The resistance between E and F increases (except for ferromagnetic materials) when the magnetic field increases. Maximum increase is of the order of 10%. (See Gauss Effect.)

NERNST EFFECT

I. Description

When heat flows across the lines of magnetic force, there is observed an electromotive force in the mutually perpendicular direction.

II. Illustration

Applying an alternating magnetic field would give a value of a-c voltage that would be proportional to the temperature gradient.

III. Magnitude

The expression for the Nernst effect in terms of the Nernst effect coefficient, Q, is:

$$E_A - E_B = -QHb \frac{dT}{dx}$$

where E_A = potential at A
E_B = potential at B
H = magnetic field intensity
b = width of material
$\frac{dT}{dx}$ = temperature gradient

For tellurium Q has a value of 3.6×10^{-9} volt/gauss °C.

RIGHI-LEDUC EFFECT

I. Description

When heat flows across the lines of magnetic force, there is a transverse temperature gradient.

II. Illustration

The temperature difference between A and B is proportional to the quantity of heat flowing.

III. Magnitude

The expression for the Righi-Leduc effect in terms of the Righi-Leduc effect coefficient, S, is:

$$T_A - T_B = -SHb \frac{dT}{dx}$$

where T_A — temperature at A
T_B — temperature at B
H — magnetic field intensity

b — width of material

$\dfrac{dT}{dx}$ — temperature gradient

The Righi-Leduc effect coefficient for iron is $S = 6 \times 10^{-7}$ gauss^{-1}, and for tellurium, $S = 62 \times 10^{-7}$ gauss $^{-1}$.

SUPPLEMENTARY THERMOMAGNETIC EFFECT

The thermoresistance increases with increase of magnetic field intensity.

IV. References

1. Mason, W. P., W. H. Hewitt, and R. F. Wick, "Hall Effect Modulation and Gyrators Employing Magnetic Field Independent Orientations in Germanium," *Journal of Applied Physics,* Vol. 24, No. 2, February, 1953, pp. 166–175. Use of Hall effect to measure field strengths, modulate, and to secure a nonreciprocal transmission.
2. Bhatnagar, S. S., and K. H. Mathur, *Physical Principles and Applications of Magnetochemistry,* Macmillan and Co., Ltd., London, 1935, pp. 268–293. Hall effect for solids and liquids, also a photoelectric Hall effect; pp. 293–294, Ettingshausen effect; pp. 300–301, Nernst effect.

See also Corbino Effect (an example of the Hall Effect), Magnetostrictions and Allied Effects, Magnetic Effects, Magnetic Susceptance.

Quantities

Angle	Current	Magnetic flux
Chemical compositions	Heat flux	Temperature

GAUSS'S LAW

I. Description

Gauss's law states that for a closed surface of any shape constructed in an electric field, the number of lines of force crossing it in an outward direction is a direct function of the net positive charge inside the surface. Although this statement is intended to hold only for free space, it may be generalized to include volumes that are partially or wholly occupied by matter. In these cases, the term net positive charge should be the algebraic sum of both the free and induced charges enclosed by the surface.

II. Illustration

Gauss's law greatly simplifies many problems involving the calculation of electric fields. Examples include the calculation of the capacitance in devices having simple geometric shapes, and the calculation of fields about transmission lines. It is also the fundamental relation used in the derivation of many other relations in electricity.

III. Magnitude

There are two equations commonly employed to express Gauss's law. One uses the concept of the electric field vector, E, and the other employs the electric displacement vector D. They are:

$$\oint E \cos \phi \, dA = \frac{1}{\epsilon_0} \Sigma q \quad \text{and} \quad \oint D \cos \phi \, dA = \Sigma q$$

where $E \cos \phi$ = the component of electric field intensity normal to the surface, volts/meter

A = surface area, square meters

ϵ_0 = the permittivity of free space, 8.85×10^{-12} farad/meter

D = displacement, coulomb/meter^2

Σq = the net positive charge, coulombs

$D \cos \phi$ = normal component of displacement, coulomb/meter^2

This same law is applicable to magnetic fields:

$$\oint \mu H \, dA = 4\pi \Sigma m$$

where μ = permeability

m = magnetic poles inside surface

H = magnetic field intensity

IV. References

1. Sears, F. W., *Principles of Physics,* Addison-Wesley Publishing Co., Cambridge, Mass., 1951, Vol. II, pp. 35, 181.
2. Boast, W. B., *Principles of Electric and Magnetic Fields,* Harper and Bros., New York, 1948, Vol. 1, p. 38. (A 1950 edition of Volume II is also useful.)
3. Skilling, H. H., *Fundamentals of Electric Waves,* John Wiley and Sons, New York, 2nd Ed., 1948, p. 39.

Quantities

Angle	Charge	Electric flux	Magnetic flux
Area	Dielectric constant	Length	Permeability

GEIGER-NUTTAL RULE

I. Description

This rule deals with the range of alpha particles.

The longest-lived radioactive elements produce lower energy alpha particles than do the short-lived elements. The empirical facts were first correlated in the Geiger-Nuttal rule which states that, when the logarithm of the disintegration constant is plotted against the logarithm of the range for the alpha emitting members in the same radioactive series, an approximately straight line is obtained.

II. Illustration

Natural alpha particle emission represented a difficult theoretical problem when the empirical facts calculated in the Geiger-Nuttal rule were compared to the scattering of alpha particles by the same nucleus. Coulomb's law indicates the need for the existence of a definite minimum energy level of alpha particles before escape from the nucleus. This is backed up by the scattered evidence of alpha particles aimed at the nucleus. However, the Geiger-Nuttal rule data shows alpha particles with about one-half the escape energy. By the application of wave mechanic techniques, the paradox was resolved, for there exists a definite probability that an alpha particle can leak through the Coulomb potential barrier; this leak has been termed the tunnel effect. Further manipulation of wave mechanic techniques produces a theoretical form of the Geiger-Nuttal rule.

III. Magnitude

The rule is expressed thus:

$$\log \lambda = A \log R + B$$

where λ = decay constant of radioactive material
R = range of particle (in air usually)
A = a constant, the same for each series of radioactive decay elements
B = a constant
T = half-life; i.e., $T = \dfrac{0.693}{\lambda}$

Some examples from the thorium series illustrate this relation:

Radioelement	Range (Alpha)	Half-Life
Thorium (Th^{232})	2.8 cm	1.39×10^{-10} yr
Radio thorium (Th^{228})	3.9 cm	1.9 yr
Thorium A ($P_0{}^{216}$)	5.6 cm	0.16 sec
Thorium C' ($P_0{}^{212}$)	8.6 cm	3.0×10^{-7} sec

IV. References

1. Glasstone, Samuel, *Sourcebook on Atomic Energy,* D. Van Nostrand Co., New York, 1950, pp. 155–156. Rule, discussion, but no examples.
2. Kaplan, J., *Nuclear Physics,* Addison-Wesley Publishing Co., Cambridge, Mass., 1956, pp. 272–281. Theory and wave mechanics analyses.

Quantities

Chemical	Length	Time
composition	Radiation	Velocity
Energy (K.E.)		

GIBBS THEORY OF EQUILIBRIA (Phase Rule)

I. Description

Phase rule defines conditions of equilibrium as a relationship between the number of phases and the components of a system. A system has only three independently variable factors or degrees of freedom—temperature, pressure, and concentration of the components of the system.

II. Illustration

The number of phases of a system are the homogeneous mechanically separable and physically distinct portions of a heterogeneous system. While the number of phases capable of existence will vary from system to system, there can never be more than one gas or vapor phase since all gases are miscible. A heterogeneous solid mixture forms as many phases as there are substances present.

III. Magnitude

A system consisting of n compounds can exist in $n + 2$ phases, only when the temperature, pressure, and concentration have fixed values; if there are n components in $n + 1$ phases, equilibrium can exist while one of the factors varies; and if there are only n phases, two of the varying factors may be arbitrarily fixed:

$$P + F = C + 2$$

where P = number of phases which are homogeneous, mechanically separable and distinct

F = degrees of freedom which must be fixed to define the system's condition

C = smallest number of components, usually elements

IV. Reference

1. Zemansky, Mark W., *Heat and Thermodynamics*, McGraw-Hill Book Co., New York, 1951. A very complete discussion of principles and problems. Applies the theory to chemical reactions as well as physical chemistry.
   See also Le Châtelier's Law.

Quantities

Concentration   Pressure   Temperature

Physical Laws and Effects

GLADSTONE AND DALE'S LAW

I. Description

The refractive index of a material changes with a change in the density of the material and in the same way. That is, as a material expands, its index of refraction decreases.

II. Illustration

A change in temperature will alter the density of a material, and thus change the index of refraction. Since applied forces also change the density, this effect may be used to determine localized stresses. Either formula works for gases at moderate pressures.

III. Magnitude

The equation for this effect is:

$$\frac{n - 1}{\rho} = c$$

Another formula for the same phenomenon by Lorentz and Lorentz is:

$$\frac{n^2 - 1}{n^2 + 2} \cdot \frac{1}{\rho} = c'$$

where n = refractive index
   ρ = density
   c, c' = constants

Since the density variations for changes in temperature are slight, the magnitude of this effect is small; a similar statement is true for the effect of forces. For variations in temperature the magnitudes of the refractive index are given for three materials:

INDEX OF REFRACTION

Temperature	Carbon Disulfide	Water	Ether
0°C	1.6442	1.3330	—
10	1.6346	1.3327	1.3592
20	1.6261	1.3320	1.3545
30	1.6182	1.3309	1.3495
40	1.6103	1.3297	—
50	—	1.3280	—
60	—	1.3259	—

For carbon dioxide, the density change is:

Density	$n - 1$ ($\lambda = 5790$ A)
0.11558	0.02645
0.71235	0.1659

IV. Reference

1. Preston, Thomas A., *The Theory of Light,* Macmillan and Co., Ltd., London, 1929, pp. 155–163. The law, discussion, and magnitude.

See also Snell's Law.

Quantities

Angle	Color	Index of	Strain
Chemical composition	Density	refraction	Temperature

GRAHAM'S LAW

(Other names applied to this phenomenon are van't Hoff, Pfeffer, atmolysis, diffusion, osmosis, dialysis)

I. Description

A. The quantity of a gas which passes through a porous diaphragm in a given time varies inversely as the square root of the molecular weight of the gas or its density.

B. The rates at which gases diffuse are not the same for all gases, but are inversely proportional to the square root of their densities. The rate is also proportional to the absolute temperature. This movement of gas need not require a porous diaphragm to be termed diffusion.

C. The osmotic pressure produced by a substance in dilute solution is equal to the pressure which this substance would exert if it alone occupied, in a gaseous state, the volume of the solution. The pressure is independent of the nature of the solvent.

II. Illustration

The common name for this phenomenon is *osmosis*. Gases (as well as liquids) exhibit selective diffusion through suitable partitions or membranes. Partitions may be selected that will allow the smaller but not the larger molecules to pass. Sizable pressures may be built up on the sides near the larger molecules. When this process is used to separate gases, it is termed atmolysis. Diffusion is employed in some gas refrigerators which use heat to cool the interior.

III. Magnitude

Hydrogen will diffuse four times as fast as oxygen. This follows from the kinetic theory from the fact that molecules of various kinds have the same mean kinetic energy, and hence their mean square speeds are inverse ratios of their masses.

A 6% sugar solution and water will develop an osmotic pressure of 307.5 cm of mercury.

IV. References

1. Hodgman, Charles D., *Handbook of Chemistry and Physics,* Chemical Rubber Publishing Co., Cleveland, Ohio, 1955. Tables of diffusion coefficient and osmotic pressures.
2. Atkinson, E., Translation of *Ganot's Physics,* William Wood and Co., New York, 1910, pp. 437–441. A qualitative description with examples.
3. Page Leigh, *Introduction to Theoretical Physics,* D. Van Nostrand Co., New York, 1935, pp. 348–351. Mathematical treatment of coefficient of diffusion.

See also Electro-osmosis, Fick's Law.

Quantities

Chemical	Flow	Liquid	Temperature
composition	Gas	Pressure	Time
Concentration			

GROUP DISPLACEMENT LAW

I. Description

The emission of particles by a radioactive element changes the position of the element in the periodic table. The emission of an alpha

(α) ray moves the element two places to the left of the parent, the emission of a beta (β) particle moves the resultant one place to the right in the periodic table. This law is also known as the Fajans-Soddy-Russell displacement law.

II. Illustration

This effect may be illustrated by the thorium series:

Radioelement	Symbol	Atomic Number	Radiation	Half-Life
Thorium	Th^{232}	90	α	1.39×10^{10} yr
Mesothorium I	Ra^{228}	88	β	6.7 yr
Mesothorium II	Ac^{228}	89	β	6.13 hr
Radiothorium	Th^{228}	90	α	1.90 yr
Thorium X	Ra^{224}	88	α	3.64 days
Th. emanation	Rn^{220}	86	α	54.5 sec
Thorium A	Po^{216}	84	α	0.16 sec
Thorium B 0.014%	Pb^{212}	82	$\beta + \alpha$	10.6 hr
Astatine-216	At^{216}	85	α	3×10^4 sec
Thorium C	Bi^{212}	83	$\beta + \alpha$	60.5 min
66.3% Thorium C'	Po^{212}	84	α	3×10^{-7} sec
Thorium C''	Tl^{202}	81	β	3.1 min
Thorium D (end product)	Pb^{208}	82	Stable	—

III. Reference

1. Glasstone, Samuel, *Sourcebook on Atomic Energy*, D. Van Nostrand Co., New York, 1950, pp. 176–179. Law, examples.

See also Radioactivity, Fission.

Quantities

Charge	Emissivity	Mass	Time
Chemical composition	Energy (P.E.)	Radiation	

HENRY'S LAW

I. Description

The quantity of a gas (either weight or volume at normal temperature and pressure) dissolved by a given volume of a given liquid at a given temperature is directly proportional to the pressure under which the absorption takes place and vice versa.

The quantity of gas which a liquid can dissolve is independent of the nature and of the quantity of other gases which it may already hold in solution.

II. Illustration

The law holds quite exactly for gases of moderate solubility which do not chemically combine with the water as do ammonia or hydrogen chloride. The solution of gases in water is usually exothermic.

III. Magnitude

The amount of gas which may be absorbed is proportional to the temperature of the fluid. One cc of water at 0°C will hold 0.0489 cc oxygen at 1 atm pressure, but at 25°C will absorb only 0.0285 cc. Similar figures for 99.7% pure ethyl alcohol are 0.2337 and 0.2171 cc oxygen absorbed showing that the effect varies from solute to solute.

IV. References

1. MacDougall, Frank H., *Physical Chemistry,* The Macmillan Co., New York, 1952, pp. 347–352. Law with examples.

Quantities

Chemical	Liquid	Pressure	Volume
composition	Mass	Temperature	
Gas			

HERTZ EFFECT

(Also known as Wiedemann and Ebert effect)

I. Description

A. Hertz found that a disruptive discharge between two conductors is facilitated by exposing the air space across which the discharge takes place to the influence of ultraviolet light. Wiedemann and Ebert proved that the seat of this action is at the cathode and that the light produces no effect when the cathode is shielded from its influence, however brightly the rest of the line of discharge may be illuminated. The magnitude of the effect depends on the gas surrounding the cathode. This is also known as the Ebert effect.

B. Certain substances, when negatively charged, lose their charge when illuminated with ultraviolet light, and if originally uncharged, they acquire a positive charge as a result of the illumination. The more electropositive the metal in the contact potential series, the longer the wavelength to which it will respond photoelectrically. This is also known as the Elster effect and Geitel effect.

II. Magnitude

This effect was the first in a long chain of discoveries that have led to the present-day photoelectric theory. See Photoelectric Effects for order of magnitude.

III. Reference

1. Richtmyer, F. K., and E. H. Kennard, *Introduction to Modern Physics*, McGraw-Hill Book Co., New York, 1955. Original experiment and several subsequent ones.
   See also Photoelectric Effects.

Quantities

Charge   Current   Light   Radiation

=====

HOOKE'S LAW

I. Description

As long as the strain is kept below a certain limit for each material, called the proportional limit, the stress is proportional to the strain, and hence, the ratio of stress to the strain (i.e., the elasticity) is a constant. The elastic limit is the limit of stress within which no permanent deformation occurs.

II. Illustration

This law is the basis of spring type scales, the deflection of the spring being proportional to the weight applied. This is also the fundamental assumption for all stress analysis.

III. Magnitude

Hooke's Law is expressed by:

$$\frac{F}{x} = K$$

where F = force per unit area (stress)

x = deformation per unit length (strain)

K = Young's modulus

Most wrought materials follow this law closely. Other materials such as wood also follow the law well.

Exceptions to the law include concrete, copper, cast iron, etc., which have proportional limits below the elastic limit.

	Yield Strength, psi	Young's Modulus, psi
Brass	25,000	13,000,000
Beryllium	60,000	19,000,000
Steel (carbon SAE 1040)	50,000	30,000,000

For steel there will be a decrease in length of 1 part in 30,000,000 for one psi.

For some materials an elastic after-effect was shown in 1825 by Wilhelm Weber where Hooke's law is slightly invalid.

IV. References

1. Maleev, V. L., *Machine Design,* International Textbook Co., Scranton, Pennsylvania, 1946, Chapter 3.
2. Faires, V. M., *Design of Machine Elements,* The Macmillan Co., New York, 1946, Chapter 1.
3. Hodgman, Charles D., *Handbook of Chemistry and Physics,* Chemical Rubber Publishing Co., Cleveland, Ohio, 1955. Elastic constants for solids.

See also Elastic Limit.

Quantities

Area	Force	Length	Strain	Stress

IDEAL GAS LAWS

I. Description*

There are a number of related laws regarding an ideal gas behavior. For the following laws, the nomenclature to be used is:

P = pressure
T = temperature (absolute)
W = weight of the gas
R = the gas constant
C = a constant
V = volume

Any consistent system of units may be employed.

Avogadro's Law. Equal volumes of all gases at the same temperature and pressure contain the same number of molecules, which for a mole of gas at standard pressure and temperature is 6.023×10^{23}.

Boyle's Law (also Mariotti's Law). If the temperature is constant, the volume of a given quantity of gas varies inversely as the pressure upon it.

$$PV = C_1$$

This equation is approximately true for actual gases and holds for low and medium pressures.

Charles' Law. If the volume of a given mass of gas is held constant, the pressure is proportional to the absolute temperature.

$$\frac{dP}{dT} = C_2$$

The change in volume of the container (expansion) must usually be considered also with the temperature change.

Gay Lussac's Law. This law is very similar to Charles' law.

---

* *Editor's note.* Many engineers are aware of these laws and thus for simplicity only a description and reference have been included.

$$V_1 = V_0(1 + aT)$$

where V_0 = original volume of gas

V_1 = volume of gas at any temperature

T = temperature difference for V_0 and V_1

a = constant (for °Kelvin or Centigrade)

air $a = 0.0036706$

hydrogen $a = 0.0036613$

(both about 1/273)

Ideal Gas Law. By combining the laws of Charles and Boyle, the ideal gas law may be derived:

$$PV = WRT$$

Real gases closely approximate an ideal gas as long as pressures and temperatures are not excessive so that condensation does not occur, since in an ideal gas the molecules do not attract each other. For these extreme conditions see van der Waals' equation. This ideal gas law also applies to mixtures of gases which do not react chemically. Some critical temperatures (see State and Change of State) which limit this law are:

	°C
Steam	374
Sulfur dioxide	157
Ammonia	132
Carbon dioxide	31

Dalton's Law of Partial Pressures. In a mixture of gases, each gas exerts the same pressure that it would if it were present alone in the volume occupied by the mixture. That is, for a mixture of gases, the total pressure is the sum of the partial pressures. This law holds true only when the ideal gas laws are valid. (See Raoult's Law and Henry's Law.)

Van der Waals' Equation. This equation considers that the molecules in a gas attract each other, hence is more useful than the ideal gas law.

$$\left(P + \frac{a}{V^2}\right)(V - b) = RT$$

where a = constant, effect of molecular attraction

b = constant, effect of volume of molecules

II. References

1. MacDougall, Frank H., *Physical Chemistry,* The Macmillan Co., New York, 1952, p. 137, Avogadro's number, pp. 60–68, van der Waals' equation and ideal gas law derivation.
2. Page, Leigh, *Introduction to Theoretical Physics,* D. Van Nostrand Co., New York, 1935, pp. 301–4, 331–353. A mathematical treatment of the properties of ideal gases, pp. 309–311. Mathematical treatment of van der Waals' equation. (Ed. note— 1935 Ed. more complete on this subject than subsequent editions.)
3. Hodgman, Charles D. (Editor), *Handbook of Chemistry and Physics,* Chemical Rubber Publishing Co., Cleveland, Ohio, 1955. Constants for van der Waals' equation.

Quantities

Gas	Mass	Pressure	Temperature	Volume

IMPEDANCE / FREQUENCY

I. Description

The impedance of a circuit is its total resistance to the flow of an electric current. This impedance for a circuit containing either inductance or capacitance varies with frequency. The magnitude of the impedance of a pure inductance is directly proportional to the frequency of the voltage impressed upon it; the impedance of a pure capacitive element is inversely proportional to the frequency of the impressed voltage.

When using capacitance and inductance together, it is possible to create circuits with either very high or very low impedance at a desired frequency.

II. Illustration

By holding the voltage constant across either an inductance or a capacitance, the current through the impedance would be a measure of electrical frequency.

The combination of a capacitor and an inductance in a series or a parallel resonance circuit resonates at a frequency determined by their value. This principle is used to tune all radio and television receivers as well as separate carrier frequency channels.

III. Magnitude

The magnitude of inductive impedance is proportional to the frequency. For an inductance of 1 henry and a frequency of 1 radian/second the impedance is 1 ohm, and is expressed:

$$Z = j\omega L$$

where L = inductance in henrys
ω = frequency in radians per sec
$\omega = 2\pi f$
f = frequency in cycles per sec
Z = impedance in ohms
$j = \sqrt{-1}$

The magnitude of capacitive impedance is inversely proportional to frequency. For a capacitance of 1 microfarad and a frequency of 1 radian/second, the impedance is 1 megohm, and is expressed:

$$Z = -j\frac{1}{\omega C}$$

where C = capacitance in farads

For a resonant circuit, if the resistance or circuit losses are small, the frequency of resonance is given by:

$$f = \frac{1}{2\pi\sqrt{LC}}$$

IV. Reference

1. Hehre, Frederick W. and George T. Harness, "Alternating Current," *Electrical Circuits and Machinery, Vol. II,* John Wiley and Sons, New York, 1942. Pp. 26–30, inductance in d-c and a-c circuits. Pp. 31–38, capacitors, construction and effects in d-c and a-c circuits.

Quantities

Capacitance   Frequency   Inductance

INTERFERENCE

I. Description

For light, interference produces a number of colored or dark bands depending on whether white or monochromatic light is used. These result from interference between two light sources a short distance apart, or the same light traveling through two slightly different path lengths. In sound, this phenomenon is termed beats, but is then caused by excitation of two slightly different frequencies.

II. Illustration

Two mirrors side by side, but not quite in the same plane, were used by Fresnel to produce these fringes. Two glass plates at slight angles to each other may also be used. Grazing incidence of light on a mirror is another means of producing fringes. Thin films also illustrate the interference of light (Newton's rings) because of the difference in path length from the upper and lower surfaces of the film for reflections. Interference films are sometimes placed on mirrors so that only a selected bandwidth is reflected. Beats are used in musical chords to produce pleasing tones. Loran is a radio navigational system using interference between two transmitters.

III. Magnitude

In order that the interference patterns of light may be visible, the path lengths must not differ by more than a few wavelengths. Because of this small allowable deviation, the fringes may be used to determine the flatness of a surface to a few millionths of an inch.

Thin films are produced on tantalum foils oxidized in the process of making electrolytic capacitors, the film color being a rather direct indication of the d-c formation voltage and formation temperature.

IV. References

1. Preston, Thomas A., *The Theory of Light,* Macmillan and Co., Ltd., London, 1929, pp. 164–241. History and discussion of many ways to produce interference bands for light.
2. Sugg, Ronald E., "An Interferometer for Examining Polished Surfaces," *Mechanical Engineering,* Vol. 75, No. 8, August, 1953, pp. 629–631. Industrial use of interferometer.
3. Sugg, R. E., "Micro Interferometry for Surface Measurements," *Product Engineering,* Vol. 23, No. 8, pp. 156–157. Interference applied to measuring a very flat surface.

See also Diffraction.

Quantities

| Frequency | Length | Light | Radiation | Sound |

JOHNSEN-RAHBEK and/or WINSLOW EFFECT

I. Description

Scientists have found that when two conductors are separated by a semi-conductor and a voltage is applied to the conductors, the friction between the conductors and the semi-conductor increases. When the semi-conductor is a solid, the effect is called the Johnsen-Rahbek effect and when the semi-conductor is a liquid the effect is called the Winslow effect. This configuration is a capacitor and there is an attractive force between the electrodes. Naturally, this force increases the friction force parallel to the face of the electrode, but in actual practice the frictional force increases faster than this attractive force.

The theory indicates that the application of a voltage across a semi-conducting fluid causes particles (such as finely divided materials, molecules, etc.) to form conducting chains, thus increasing the viscosity of the liquid. Hence, it is seen that this phenomenon is quite similar to the magnetic fluid coupling, although the effect is not so strong because the attractive properties of the particles are less. Similar reasoning may be applied to the solid semi-conductor unit because the semi-conductor may be saturated with an electrolyte which could act as the fluid. For a small air gap the air could form conducting chains. The effect is also present with dry semi-conductors.

II. Illustrations

Materials that have been used:

Conductors. Any good conductor that can be given a smooth flat surface.

Semi-conductors. (1) Solid: Agate, lithographic stone, sintered magnesium oxide and titanium dioxide. (2) Liquid: pyranol, inerteen, mineral oil and lanolin.

Applications of the fluid type semi-conductors are quite well covered in U. S. Patent 2,417,850 of April 14, 1942.

The device may be used similar to a magnetic fluid type clutch. The unit will require less power as the effect depends on voltage and not on current, but its torque capacity is considerably less than a magnetic type clutch.

One of the more promising applications of this effect is a voltage operated low torque relay.

This effect has been applied to loudspeakers where the audiosignal is used to change the friction between a spring loaded ribbon attached to the loudspeaker diaphragm and an agate cylinder rotating at constant speed.

III. Magnitude

The magnitudes of this effect are hard to determine as most of the work done so far has been experimental and not analytical. Also there has been a wide variation in materials used which gave different magnitudes.

One experiment showed that the friction force between a rotating agate cylinder and a strip of tinfoil in contact with 180 degrees of the cylinder surface varied as the fifth power of the voltage between 25 and 300 volts.

The order of magnitude of this force is grams, not pounds.

IV. References

1. *Science Abstracts "A", 1934* (Vol. XXXVII), Item 3909. Also Vol. A, 1928, item 3099. Abstracts and formulas from foreign papers.

2. *Journal of Applied Physics,* Vol. 21, May, 1950, pp. 402–413. The effect for liquids.

3. Johnsen, Alfred and Rahbek, Knud, "A Physical Phenomena and its Application to Telegraphy, Telephony, etc.," *The Journal of the Scientific Institute of Electrical Engineers,* Vol. 61, 1923. pp. 713–725, qualitative description and uses. Mentions electromatographic effect.

Quantities

Chemical composition   Electric flux   Friction   Liquid   Potential

JOULE'S LAW

I. Description

The heat produced by the passage of an electric current through a solid metallic conductor is proportional to the resistance of the conductor, the square of the current and the time, or to the product of the applied emf, the current and the time.

II. Illustration

A method of measuring high-frequency current is to heat a thermocouple with a series resistance. The temperature differential between thermocouple junctions is a measure of the high-frequency current.

III. Magnitude

The heat developed is:

$$JH = RI^2t = EIt$$

where J = Joule's dynamic equivalent of heat
H = number of heat units
R = resistance of the element
I = current through the resistance
t = time (usually seconds or hours)
E = voltage across the resistance *only*

The equation:

$$Wt = RI^2t$$

where W = watts (rate of using energy)

holds for both a-c and d-c circuits. If t is in seconds, the results are watt seconds, if t is in hours, the energy is in watt hours. One thousand watts consumed for one hour is a kilowatt hour.

For a circuit having a resistance of 1 ohm and a current of 10 amp, the rate of heat generation will be 100 watts. For modifications of this law, see Thomson Effect and Benedict Effect.

IV. Reference

  1. Hausmann, E., and E. Slack, *Physics*, D. Van Nostrand Co., New York, 1948, pp. 379–380. Description and examples.

Quantities

Current	Heat flux	Power	Time
Energy (K.E.)	Potential	Resistivity	

═══════════════════════════════════════

JOULE-THOMSON EFFECT

(Also known as Joule-Kelvin effect)

─────────────

I. Description

When a gas expands through a throttling device, the temperature of the gas is lowered or raised depending on the temperature at which the process takes place and upon the physical properties of the gas.

There is a molecular force between molecules of a gas. When the gas expands, the molecules become more widely separated. In order for the expansion to go on, the force between the molecules must be overcome, which is an action requiring energy. This energy is derived from the heat energy of the gas itself; so if the gas uses its own heat for expansion, its content of heat is reduced and its temperature is lowered.

At ordinary temperatures, certain gases such as hydrogen, when undergoing the same process, will have a heat rise instead of drop. This is because all gases have a so-called inversion temperature. Below this temperature a gas will cool on being expanded, and above this temperature the gas will gain heat. Hydrogen has a low inversion temperature, so its initial temperature has to be reduced below ordinary temperatures (about $-183°C$) before the Joule-Thomson effect takes place.

II. Illustration

Practical use of the Joule-Thomson effect is used in making liquid air by the Linde process as well as in refrigerating cycles.

III. Magnitude

The fall in temperature for air by the Joule-Thomson effect is approximately:

$$\text{Fall in temperature} = \frac{P_1 - P_2}{4} \frac{(289)}{(T_1)}$$

where P_1 = pressure in atmospheres before throttling
P_2 = pressure in atmospheres after throttling
T_1 = temperature before throttling in °K

The rate of change of temperature with respect to pressure under the conditions of the Joule-Thomson experiment is called the Joule-Thomson coefficient, J.T.C.,

$$\text{J.T.C.} = \frac{(dT)}{(dP)}\bigg]_h$$

where h denotes constant enthalpy.

When a gas is at its inversion temperature the J.T.C. is 0.

IV. References

1. MacDougall, Frank H., *Physical Chemistry*, The Macmillan Co., New York, 1952, pp. 40–42. Primarily a mathematical treatment.
2. Zemansky, Mark W., *Heat and Thermodynamics*, McGraw-Hill Book Co., New York, 1951, pp. 249–258. Effect and some uses.

Quantities

Energy (K.E.)	Gas	Pressure	Volume
Enthalpy	Heat flux	Temperature	

KELVIN'S PRINCIPLE FOR FLUID DROPS

I. Description

The minimum size of liquid drops which may exist or form in a supersaturated vapor decreases as the degree of supersaturation increases.

II. Illustration

The nuclei which must be available to condense supersaturated vapors must equal the minimum size drops for these same conditions. This effect is used in the Wilson cloud chamber to detect ions formed by subatomic collisions and also to sort particles according to size.

III. Magnitude

The minimum size of drops which may exist or may be formed is given by the expression:

$$\log e \frac{P}{P_s} = \frac{2S}{RT\rho r}$$

where P = the pressure of the supersaturated vapor
P_s = the normal pressure of saturation on a flat surface
S = the surface tension
R = a constant

T = the absolute temperature
ρ = density of the fluid
r = radius of the drop

For water, if a drop is 10^{-4} mm in diameter, the ratio P over P_s is 1.02, while for a drop diameter of 10^{-6} mm, P to P_s is 10.2.

IV. References

1. Ewing, J. A., *Thermodynamics,* Cambridge University Press, London, 1946, pp. 343–346. A mathematical discussion. *See also* Surface Tension.

Quantities

Density	Liquid	Temperature
Length	Surface tension	Vapor pressure

===

KEPLER'S LAWS

I Description

Kepler's laws, which describe free elliptic motion of planets, are three in number:

1. The planets move about the sun in ellipses, the sun at one focus.

2. The radius vector joining a planet with the sun describes equal areas during equal times.

3. The cubes of the mean distances of the planets from the sun are proportional to the squares of their times of revolution about the sun.

These laws can be generalized to include all free-body revolutions about an attracting point if the force of attraction is inversely proportional to the intervening distance.

The generalized laws are:

1. The point toward which the acceleration is directed is at one of the two foci of the path ellipse.

2. A radius-vector drawn from that point to the moving body sweeps over equal areas in equal times as the body moves.

3. The time taken to perform a complete revolution in the elliptical path is proportional to the square root of the cube of the mean distance from the central point.

II. Illustration

These laws guided Newton in his gravitational researches.

The conservation of moment of momentum theorem, known otherwise as the Law of areas, states that the magnitude of the momentum is equal to the product of the mass and twice the area swept over in unit time by a radius vector when the only forces acting on it are central forces; that is, forces not producing torques. Applied to planets around the sun, this is Kepler's first law.

III. Magnitude

This law can be applied to the calculation of the orbits of submicroscopic particles as well as astronomical bodies.

IV. References

1. Karman and Biot, *Mathematical Methods in Engineering*, Mc-Graw-Hill Book Co., New York, 1940, p. 77.

2. Page, Leigh, *Introduction to Theoretical Physics*, D. Van Nostrand Co., New York, 1952, pp. 107–116. Mathematics of motion under inverse square form of attraction.

Quantities

Acceleration	Area	Force	Length	Time

KERR EFFECT (ELECTROSTATIC)

I. Description

Certain substances which normally are optically isotropic become double refracting when subjected to an electric field.* (The index of refraction for light whose electric vector is parallel to the applied field is different from light whose electric vector is perpendicular to the applied field.) Thus, plane polarized light whose electric vector has components both parallel and perpendicular to the applied electric field will become elliptically polarized when passing through the substance which exhibits the Kerr effect.

II. Illustration

Kerr effect may be used as an optical shutter. This is accomplished by placing before the Kerr cell a polarizer that is oriented so that the electric vector of the light is at an angle of 45° (for best results) with the electric field. An analyzer is placed behind the Kerr cell and is adjusted for zero light passage when no electric field is applied to the Kerr cell. The shutter is then opened by applying a voltage to the Kerr cell. Modern pulse techniques permit very accurate timing of shutter opening and closing (5×10^{-9} seconds).

III. Magnitude

The phase difference angle is given by the following equation:

$$\sigma = 2KLE^2$$

where σ = time phase difference angle (radians) between polarized light
        components
    K = Kerr constant of substance
    L = path under influence of electric field (cm)
    E = electric field (cgs. units)

* *Note.* Cotton and Mouton observed this same effect with a magnetic field in 1905.

The Kerr constant of most substances is a function of both temperature and the wavelength of the transmitted light.

A Kerr cell using nitrobenzene as the fluid in a unit 2 cm long and having a spacing between plates of 0.5 cm will require approximately 15,000 volts (mks units) to fully open the shutter. This will pass one-fourth of the incident nonpolarized light.

Substance	Kerr Constant	Resistivity, ohms-cm	Dielectric Constant
Carbon disulfide CS_2	3.6×10^{-7}	10^{16}	2.5
Chloroform $CHCl_3$	-3.2×10^{-7}	10^8	5.0
Acetone C_3H_6O	16×10^{-7}	10^7	20.0
Nitrobenzene $C_6H_5NO_2$	400×10^{-7}	10^{10}	36.0

Time lag for nitrobenzene is less than 10^{-9} second. Some glasses have time lags as high as 30 seconds.

IV. Reference

1. Preston, T., *The Theory of Light*, Macmillan and Co., Ltd., London, 1928, pp. 466–468. Qualitative description.

Quantities

Angle	Electric flux	Light	Polarization	Translu-
Chemical	Frequency	Opaqueness	Time	cence
composition				

KERR MAGNETO-OPTIC EFFECT

I. Description

When plane polarized light is incident on the pole of an electromagnet, polished so as to act like a mirror, the plane of polarization of the reflected light is not the same when the magnet is "on" as when it is "off." It is found that the direction of rotation depends upon the direction of light polarization and the angle of incidence. The rotation from the nonmagnetized plane will be proportional to the flux density leaving the polished metallic surface.

II. Illustration

This effect can be used to detect the strength of magnetic flux density, type of material, and frequency of incident light.

This effect can also be used to measure the intensity of magnetic flux leaving a magnetic pole. The degree of rotation of the plane of polarization will be the true indication of the flux density. This rotation may be used to examine thin surface films, since the reflection and the rotation are surface phenomena.

III. Magnitude

For surfaces of the following materials, the angular rotation is given:

Fe $= 0.014'/$gauss

Co $= 0.015'/$gauss $= 5300$ A

Ni $= 0.016'/$gauss

IV. References

1. Wood, R. W., *Physical Optics,* Macmillan and Co., New York, 1934, p. 401.

2. Bhatmayer, S. S., and K. N. Mathur, *Physical Principles and Applications of Magneto-chemistry*, Macmillan and Co., Ltd., London, 1935, pp. 278–279. Various conditions and results.

Quantities

Angle	Color	Magnetic flux	Reflection
Chemical composition	Light	Polarization	

KIRCHHOFF'S LAWS

I. Description

First Law. At any point in a circuit there is as much current flowing away from the point as there is flowing to it.

Second Law. The sum of the several IR drops around any one path of an electric circuit equals the sum of the emfs impressed on the same path.

II. Illustration

This law is basic to all circuit analysis and to most network theorems.

III. Magnitude

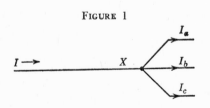

FIGURE 1

For the first law, the circuit in Figure 1, is expressed:

$$I = I_a + I_b + I_c$$

Otherwise, there would be a charge build-up at the junction X.

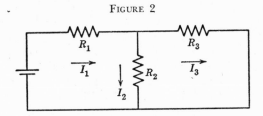

FIGURE 2

The second law, the circuit in Figure 2, is expressed:

$$I_1 = I_2 + I_3 \text{ (by the first law)}$$

$$E = I_1R_1 + I_2R_2 = I_1R_1 + I_3R_3$$

$$0 = I_2R_2 - I_3R_3$$

The negative sign occurs because direction of travel in the loop is opposite to that of the current.

It should be noted that Kirchhoff's laws apply to instantaneous values and for circuit (not field) problems. The law is not generally true for rms a-c values because of the phase angles encountered. If current and voltage vectors are considered, the law still holds.

IV. References

1. Timbie, William H., and Vannevar Bush, *Principles of Electrical Engineering*, John Wiley and Sons, New York, 4th Ed., 1951, Chapter 2.

Quantities

Current   Potential

KOHLRAUSCH'S LAW

(Also known as Debye-Huckel equation or
Onsager's conductance theory)

I. Description

The limiting equivalent conductance of an electrolyte is due to the sum of two migrations: that of the cations and that of the anions. These two types of ions migrate independently to produce conduction.

The equivalent conductance of strong electrolytes in extremely dilute solutions is a linear function of the square root of the concentration.

The equivalent conductance of an electrolyte is the conductance of a column 1 cm long and containing 1 mole of solute. The conductivity approaches a limiting value as the concentration of the dissolved solute approaches zero.

II. Illustration

This law describes conductance behavior of solutions, i.e., batteries, plating baths, and leveling cells. This law is also useful to determine the concentration of a solution.

III. Magnitude

The law may be expressed as:

$$\Lambda = \Lambda_0 - AC^{\frac{1}{2}}$$

where Λ = equivalent conductance
Λ_0 = limiting equivalent conductance
A = constant, depending on electrolyte and temperature
C = concentration in moles/liter

A, as determined by Onsager, is:

$$A = \left[\frac{(5.78 \times 10^5 \Lambda_0)}{(DT)^{3/2}} + \frac{58.0}{(DT)^{1/2}\eta} \right] \sqrt{2}$$

where D = dielectric constant of the solvent (free space = 1)

T = absolute temperature

η = viscosity

For HCl the conductances for concentrations up to 0.0016 mole/liter are found to within 0.05%. This expression holds poorly, however, for low concentrations of the weak electrolytes.

IV. References

1. MacDougall, Frank H., *Physical Chemistry*, The Macmillan Co., New York, 1952, pp. 515–517. Discussion with examples.
2. Dole, Malcolm, *Principles of Experimental and Theoretical Electro-Chemistry*, McGraw-Hill Book Co., New York, 1934, pp. 89–106. Debye-Huckel equations, Onsager's conductance theory, and others for concentrated solutions.

See also Wien Effect.

Quantities

Chemical composition	Current	Resistivity
Concentration	Dielectric constant	Temperature

LAMBERT'S LAW, ABSORPTION COEFFICIENT

I. Description

Radiation, including light, which has transversed any thin layer of matter perpendicular to the direction of propagation is reduced in intensity in proportion to the thickness of the layer.

Beer's law, which is an extension of Lambert's law, states that if two solutions of the same salt be made in the same solvent, the first of which is twice the concentration of the other, the absorption due to a given thickness of the first solution should be equal to that of twice the thickness of the second.

II. Illustration

The absorption coefficient of copper for certain X-rays is 13.5 cm^{-1}; X-rays in passing through 0.0513 cm thickness of copper foil will emerge only with one-half their original intensity. The effect is also of importance with thick windows as used for shielding against radioactive materials and in other test cells.

Beer's law fails to hold in all cases due to a reaction between the solvent and solute or a change in the molecular state of the solute with changes in its concentration, i.e., "packing" of the molecules.

III. Magnitude

The flux density after having penetrated the medium to a distance x is:

$$\ln \frac{I}{I_0} = - ax$$

in which I_0 is the flux density upon entrance into the medium (i.e., $x = 0$). For true absorption, the constant a is the absorption coefficient. The law holds when scattering does not occur.

In general the absorption coefficient of a medium varies characteristically with the wavelength of the radiation, as illustrated by the absorption of X-rays in aluminum.

Wavelength, cm	Absorption Coefficient (cm^{-1})
100×10^{-11}	0.45
200	0.72
300	1.45
400	2.95
500	5.30
1000	38.00

For electrons at about the velocity of 0.2 of the velocity of light,

$$I = I_0 e^{\frac{-\alpha x}{\rho}}$$

where
x = thickness of material (cm)
c = velocity of light
α and ρ = given in table below

Material	α	ρ	$\dfrac{\alpha}{\rho}$
H_2 (760 mm)	0.467	0.000085	5610
Air (760 mm)	3.42	0.00123	2780
Al	71.50	2.7	2650
Cu	23,800	8.9	2670
Ag	32,200	10.5	3070
Au	55,600	19.3	2880

IV. References

1. Hodgman, C. D., *Handbook of Chemistry and Physics,* Chemical Rubber Publishing Co., Cleveland, 1955. Tables of coefficients.
2. Koller, Lewis R., *Ultraviolet Radiation,* John Wiley and Sons, New York, 1952, pp. 140–177. Law, examples, and materials.
3. Walsh, John W. T., *Photometry,* D. Van Nostrand Co., New York, 1953.
4. Tomaschek, *Grimsehl's Lehrbuch der Physik,* B. G. Teubner in Leipzig and Berlin, 1934, p. 31. For electrons at about 0.2 speed of light (or more), the absorption depends only on the mass of the absorber. Called Lenard's law.

Quantities

Absorption	Frequency	Light	Radiation
Chemical composition	Length	Liquid	

Le CHÂTELIER'S LAW

I. Description

If some stress (e.g., change of temperature, pressure, or concentration) is brought to bear on a system in equilibrium, the equilibrium is displaced in the direction which tends to undo the effect of the stress.

This applies to all systems and changes of the condition of equilibrium, whether physical or chemical. Other names are Law of mass action and Principle of Le Châtelier-Braun.

Chemically, this law, known as van't Hoff's principle (also van't Hoff's law), states that if the temperature of interacting substances in equilibrium is raised, the equilibrium concentrations of the reaction are changed so that the products of that reaction which absorb heat are increased in quantity; or if the temperature for such an equilibrium is lowered, the products which evolve heat in their formation are increased in amounts.

II. Illustration

Thus when a system in equilibrium is subjected to an increase in pressure, it adjusts itself so that it will occupy less volume. This will offset the pressure increase.

If ice is placed under an increased pressure, it melts because the water obtained from a given mass of it occupies less volume (regelation).

III. Magnitude

As one example of this law, if a physical system involves a condition of only a change of state, temperature, a volume change, and a pressure change, a thermodynamics relation known as the Clapeyron-Clausius equation describes the situation:

$$L = T \left(\frac{dp}{dT} \right) \Delta V$$

where L = heat for change of state
  ΔV = change in volume for change in state
  T = temperature
  dp = change in pressure

IV. References

1. MacDougall, Frank H., *Physical Chemistry*, The Macmillan Co., New York, 1943. Pp. 301–302, Law of mass action; pp. 331–333, Le Châtelier's law and examples.
2. Dole, Malcolm, *Principles of Experimental and Theoretical Electro-Chemistry*, McGraw-Hill Book Co., New York, 1935, pp. 322–350. Law of mass action, mainly concerned with dissociation.
3. Taylor, Hugh S., *A Treatise on Physical Chemistry*, Vol. I. D. Van Nostrand Co., New York, 1942. Chemical and physical equilibria, with examples.
See also Gibbs Theory of Equilibria.

Quantities

Concentration   Pressure   Stress   Temperature   Volume

LEIDENFROST'S PHENOMENA

I. Description

When a liquid is boiled on a hot surface and the temperature of the surface is increased beyond the boiling temperature of the liquid, a critical temperature difference is reached where the liquid no longer wets the hot surface and is partially insulated from the surface by a layer of vapor.

II. Illustration

If a drop of water is placed on a 240°F surface, it will be evaporated rapidly. If a drop of water is placed on a 300°F surface, the drop will dance around on a film of steam and evaporate slowly. The layer of steam forms an effective insulation between the water and the hot surface.

A classical laboratory experiment is to drop water into a cup of cold sulfur dioxide within an evacuated chamber. The water will actually freeze on the surface by evaporation!

The rate of heat transfer falls off when the critical temperature is exceeded. If the hot surface was supplied by a constant source of heat and the liquid was intended to dissipate that heat, then the system would run away if the critical temperature was exceeded. The surface would get hotter and hotter while the liquid absorbed less and less heat.

III. Magnitude

The critical temperature difference for water is 45°F and the maximum heat transfer is about 400,000 Btu/hr per ft².

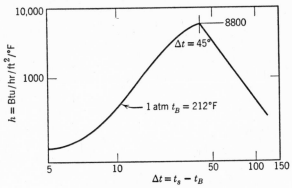

Heat transfer coefficient, h_1 for water boiling at 1 atm
for various surface temperatures, t_s

IV. Reference

1. McAdams, W. H., *Heat Transmission,* McGraw-Hill, New York, 1942, Chapter 10, p. 297.

Quantities

Boiling point   Heat flux   Liquid   Temperature

LICHTENECKERS' LAW

I. Description

This law relates the permitivity in ferroelectric mixtures. (Permitivity is the effective dielectric constant.)

II. Illustration

This law is useful in determining the dielectric constants of ferro-electric mixtures, especially when each component may have different curie temperatures.

III. Magnitude

The expression for this effect is:

$$\log K = X_1 \log K_1 + X_2 \log K_2$$

where K = permitivity of the material

X = volume percentage of components

This law does not apply when dealing with phases of widely different properties, e.g., barium titanate $(K = 1500)$, air $(K = 1)$.

IV. References

1. Popper, P., "Ceramic Dielectrics and Their Application to Capacitors for Use in Electronic Equipment," *The Proceeding of the Institution of Electrical Engineers,* Part IIA. Insulating Materials, Vol. 100, 1953, pp. 229–238. Discussion of capacitors.

Quantities

        Capacitance   Dielectric constant

LIQUID CRYSTAL PHASE

I. Description

Most substances exist in only one vapor phase, one liquid phase, and one or more crystalline phases. However, certain organic substances whose molecules are particularly polar will melt to form a milky, doubly refractive, viscous liquid called the mesomorphic phase. The term liquid crystals is also used since the molecules appear to be partially oriented layers similar to the cleavage planes of a crystal. As the temperature is raised, a second melting point is reached and the cloudy, viscous liquid abruptly changes to a clear, mobile liquid. No discontinuities appear in the other physical properties at this point.

Two types of liquid crystals are reported: the smectic and the nematic. The former show simple X-ray diffraction patterns, while the latter have interesting magnetic properties.

II. Illustration

Cholesteryl benzoate is a crystalline solid at room temperature. It melts at 145.5°C to form a cloudy, viscous liquid. At 178.5°C it abruptly transforms to a clear liquid of lower viscosity. If cholesteryl benzoate were placed between polaroids set at right angles, it would act as a light valve. Light would be transmitted only in the temperature range of 145.5 to 178.5°C when the substance was doubly refractive.

III. Magnitude

Over 250 substances have been found which go through a mesomorphic or liquid crystal phase. All of these are organic compounds having a long straight-chain construction.

IV. References

1. Taylor, H. S., *A Treatise on Physical Chemistry,* Van Nostrand Co., New York, 1942, Vol. I.

2. Bhatnazer, S. S., and Mathur, K. H., *Physical Principles and Applications of Magneto-Chemistry*, Macmillan and Co., Ltd., London, 1935, p. 350. Discussion of smectic and nematic forms.

Quantities

Chemical composition	Light	Opaqueness	Translucence
Diffraction	Liquid	Temperature	

==

LUMINESCENCE

I. Description

The conversion of energy within a material may result in luminescence—the emission of visible light. Incandescence occurs when matter is heated to a high temperature. When light is excited by some form of energy other than high temperature heat, it is called fluorescence. If light emission persists after the excitation is removed, the term phosphorescence is used.

Where electromagnetic excitation is involved, the wavelength of the emitted light is always longer than the wavelength of the absorbed light or radiation. This is Stokes's law of fluorescence.

Luminescent effects may be classified according to the types of energy excitation which cause light emission.

Heat excitation

High temperature heat (incandescence)

Electromagnetic excitation

Visible light (photoluminescence).
Ultraviolet light.

X-rays.
Gamma rays.
Infrared.
Radio waves.

Alternating electric field excitation (electroluminescence)

Particle excitation

Cathode rays (cathodoluminescence).
Radioactive emission, i.e. alpha particles, beta particles, gamma rays.
Beams of molecules, neutrons, deutrons, or positrons.

Physical change excitation

Friction or pressure (Triboluminescence).
Ultrasonic waves (Sonoluminescence).
Extreme cold.
Crystallization (Crystalluminescence).

Chemical change excitation

Oxidation.
Biological mechanisms.

Once fluorescence or phosphorescence has been excited in a material, the light emission may be slowed down, locally extinguished, or stopped altogether by various quenching means.

Light quenching mediums

Heat or infrared radiation.
Extreme cold.
Oxygen and ozone.
Minute traces of certain materials.
Strong magnetic field.

II. Illustration

Incandescence or high temperature light is generated in many ways: combustion, an electric arc, a tungsten filament, or sparks from a hammer blow. Incandescence begins at about 500°C.

Photoluminescence is often difficult to recognize since the fluorescent light adds itself to the exciting light. For example, the green tint of cheap glass is not the "color" of the glass but rather the green fluorescence of impurities in the glass. The effect is quite pronounced for solutions of organic dyes such as uranine and fluorescein.

Ultraviolet conversion to visible light represents the widest application of fluorescent materials. Fluorescent lamps are coated with a phosphor which will absorb the ultraviolet energy of the gas discharge and re-emit the energy in the visible spectrum. High visibility paints and dyes have been developed which absorb the ultraviolet in sunlight and fluoresce with a color which reinforces the color of the pigment.

X-rays were first discovered on a crude fluoroscopic screen. The present day fluoroscope screen has a coating of calcium tungstate or zinc sulfide phosphor and is bright enough for photography as well as direct observation in a darkened room.

Gamma rays and short X-rays will excite certain phosphors, but the strength and efficiency of fluorescence diminish as the excitation wavelength becomes shorter.

Infrared and radio waves may act as light-releasing agents when the energy is already present in the material. Fluorite crystals, after a preliminary exposure to light, may be warmed by infrared to luminesce with a faint white glow.

Electroluminescence is the fluorescence of a phosphor when it is subjected to an alternating electric field between two capacitor plates. The phosphor is mixed into the dielectric material and one plate of the capacitor is made of conducting glass to let the light out.   The light emitted is in phase with the a-c power absorbed by the dielectric.

Cathode rays or streams of negative particles will excite fluorescence in certain gases, liquids, and solids. The television picture tube has a screen coated with a phosphor such as zinc sulfide.

Radioactive emissions will excite fluorescence in a large number of materials. Continually luminous paints are made by mixing one part radium with 10,000 parts of zinc sulfide. Uranium is self-exciting and need not be combined with a phosphor.

Triboluminescence is observed in a small number of materials (sugar, mica, uranium salts, ice, etc.) which emit a glow when scratched, struck, or broken.

Ultrasonic waves will excite luminescence in distilled water and some aqueous solutions at a frequency of about 9 kilocycles/sec.

Extreme cold will cause pronounced fluorescence in many materials which have a feeble effect at ordinary temperatures. Some form of energy must be supplied along with the low temperature.

Crystalluminescence is observed in some solutions which emit light during the formation of crystals.

Oxidation of phosphorus at room temperatures results in a slow combustion glow. Carbon bisulfide glows at temperatures just below 180°C. Most substances have ignition temperatures occurring in the region of thermal incandescence and this effect cannot be observed.

Biological phosphorescence appears in decaying matter such as fish, insects, such as the firefly, and many deep sea animals.

Quenching of fluorescence

Heat or Infrared radiation will darken any spot that it strikes on a fluorescent screen.

Cooling will reduce the brightness and increase the duration of emission of a phosphorescent material. Extreme cold will suspend luminous activity and preserve luminous energy indefinitely.

Oxygen and ozone have a strong quenching action on fluorescent gases and liquids.

Minute traces of materials may be detected by fluorescence. For example, one-millionth of a gram of silver can quench the bright yellow fluorescence of uranium solutions.

Strong magnetic fields can quench the fluorescence of iodine vapors and a few gases.

III. Magnitude

Incandescence

At a temperature of 6500°K, the greatest portion of heat energy is

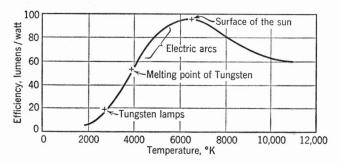

converted to visible radiation. A crude color scale is sometimes used to judge the temperatures of materials as they become luminous.

Incipient red heat	550°C	Yellowish red heat	1100°C
Dark red heat	700°C	Incipient red heat	1300°C
Bright red heat	900°C	White heat	1500°C

The efficiency of the filament lamp is 15 lumens/watt.

Ultraviolet fluorescence

Fluorescent lamps have an efficiency of 60 lumens/watt.

Radioactive fluorescence

The excitation values of radiations are approximately in these proportions:

Alpha particles (helium ions)	:	100,000
Beta particles (electrons)	:	1,000
Gamma radiation (short X-rays)	:	1

Electroluminescence

Efficiences of $\frac{1}{3}$ lumen/watt have been obtained so far. The light output is dependent on the rate of change of voltage and increases as the frequency and voltage are increased. The threshold of light emission occurs at about 25 a-c volts. At 200 a-c volts and 4000 cps an emission of 20 lumens/square foot can be excited.

IV. References

1. De Ment, J., *Fluorescent Chemicals and Their Applications,* Chemical Publishing Company, New York, 1942. 240 pages— a complete coverage of phosphors and luminous effects.
2. Wood, R. W., *Physical Optics,* Macmillan Co., New York, 1934, pp. 648–667. Theory of fluorescence.
3. Payne, E. C., E. L. Mager, and C. W. Jerome, "Electroluminescence—A New Method of Producing Light," *Illuminating Engineering,* Nov. 1950, pp. 688–693. Description of parameters and experimental results.

Quantities

Absorption	Color	Energy (K.E.)	Light	Radiation
Chemical	Emissivity	Intensity	Magnetic flux	Temperature
composition				

MAGNETIC BEHAVIOR OF MATERIALS

I. Description

If a magnetizing force is applied to a material, the ratio between the number of flux lines resulting in the material as compared with those which would result in free space is defined as the permeability of the material or μ. The value of μ defines the material.

Ferromagnetic. Strongly attracted to a magnet; $\mu \gg 1$ (may be 10^6). These materials which also have a high residual magnetism are termed permanent magnets. Temperatures near absolute zero may alter the magnetic properties of the material. Examples are iron, nickel, gadolinium, and cobalt (see Curie-Weiss law).

Paramagnetic. Slightly attracted to a magnet; $\mu > 1$. In general these materials have quite temperature sensitive behavior. Examples are oxygen and nitric oxide. This effect is small compared to ferromagnetic forces.

Diamagnetic. Repelled from the magnet; $\mu < 1$. Bismuth is an example; some types of glass are other examples. This effect produces small forces.

II. Illustration

The paramagnetic properties of oxygen are used in a continuously indicating meter to measure the percent oxygen in the gas mixture. The magnetic properties of materials have been used to analyze their substance. An anisotropy is an effect in magnets which causes them to have some easy directions of magnetization (such as length to width ratios; this directionality is attributed to atomic arrangements in a crystal).

III. References

1. Zemansky, Mark W., *Heat and Thermodynamics*, McGraw-Hill Book Co., New York, 1951. Paramagnetic materials and use of adiabatic demagnetization.

2. *Permanent Magnet Design Manual,* General Electric Co., Carboloy Publication, No. PM-101.
3. Bhatnager, S. S., and K. N. Mathur, *Physical Principles of Applications of Magneto-chemistry,* Macmillan and Co., Ltd., London, 1935. Sections of the book will be found useful for any phase of this subject.

See also Cotton-Mouton Effect, Faraday Effect (Magneto-Optical Rotation), Kerr Effect, Magnetic Effects, Photomagnetic Effect, Skin Effect, Zeeman Effect.

Quantities

Chemical composition   Magnetic flux

MAGNETIC DISPERSION OF SOUND

I. Description

Sound waves traveling in an electrically conducting plate perpendicular to a magnetic field will generate a voltage so as to reduce (Lenz's law) the longitudinal movement of the metal. This effect has two aspects: the phase velocity of the wave is increased and the mechanical stiffness of the material is increased.

II. Illustration

This voltage is masked in ferromagnetic materials by the Villari effect. The phenomenon has been observed in magnesium, aluminum, and copper.

III. Magnitude

The formula for change in phase velocity is

$$c/c_0 = 1 + \frac{40.1 d B_0^2 \sigma^{1/2}}{\rho \mu_r^{1/2} h f^{3/2}}$$

where c = phase velocity of sound with field
c_0 = phase velocity of sound
$d = 1 - e^{-sh} (\cos sh + \sin sh)$
B_0 = magnetic field intensity (Weber/m^2)
σ = conductivity
ρ = density
μ_r = relative permeability
h = thickness of the bar
f = frequency in cps

$$s = \frac{1}{\delta}$$

δ = skin depth

Material	$\sigma^{1/2}/\rho\mu_r^{1/2}$
Lithium	0.064
Calcium	0.030
Magnesium	0.028
Aluminum	0.022
Chromium	0.009
Copper	0.0085
Silver	0.0075
Iron	0.00034

As shown in the table, the effect is maximum for lithium. A magnesium alloy bar with a resonant frequency of 16.914 kc had the frequency increased by 0.238 kc upon the application of a magnetic field of 1.0 Weber/m^2.

IV. Reference

1. Robey, Donald H., "Magnetic Dispersion of Sound in Electrically Conducting Plates," *The Journal of the Acoustical Society of America*, Vol. 25, No. 4, July, 1953, pp. 603–609.

Quantities

Current	Frequency	Permeability	Sound
Density	Magnetic flux	Resistivity	Transmission (speed of sound)

MAGNETIC EFFECTS

I. Description

This is a summary of a number of magnetic effects.

Mechanical effects caused by a magnetic field (on material in field)

1. *Joule effect**—change in length due to a longitudinal field—small magnitude, sensitive to temperature and pressure, greatest for nickel (see Magnetostriction).

2. *Transverse Joule effect*—change in transverse dimensions.

3. *Change in Young's modulus.*

4. *Guillemin effect*—bending due to a field.

5. *Wiedemann effect**—twist caused by circular and longitudinal fields.

6. *Change in coefficient of rigidity* (See Magnetic Dispersion of Sound).

7. *Barrett effect*—change in volume.

8. *Gyromagnetic effect*—the recoil experienced by ferromagnetic and paramagnetic coils because of the angular momentum of the electrons in the substance.

Magnetic effects caused by mechanical stresses

1. *Villari effect**—change in induction due to stresses parallel to field; for weak fields flux is increased, for strong fields, reduced.

* Consult index for further information.

2. *Transverse Villari effect*—change in induction because of transverse stresses.

3. *Wertheim effect*—circular magnetization caused by twisting a longitudinally magnetized bar.

4. *Nagaoka-Honda effect*—change in intensity of magnetization due to volume changes.

5. *Magnetic anisotropy*—the coercive force of a magnet depends on the direction of magnetization, found by William H. Meiklyshn of General Electric Research Laboratory.

Miscellaneous

1. *Discharge tubes* (electrical)—a magnetic field will change the current through the tube.

2. *Flame*—a magnetic field tends to increase flame resistance and in some cases to affect its brightness.

3. *Fluorescent gases*—a magnetic field tends to decrease the intensity of the fluorescence. (See Luminescence.*)

4. *Chemical reactions*—some accelerated, others not, no general conclusions.

5. *Optics*—magnetic fields of a few hundred gauss applied to nematic type liquid crystals clear up the opacity of the liquid. (See Liquid Crystal Phase.*)

6. *Peltier effect*—a change has been observed in this effect under magnetic fields.

7. *Resistance change*—conductors change resistance slightly when subjected to magnetic fields.

II. Reference

1. Bhatnazer, S. S., and K. H. Mathur, *Physical Principles and Applications of Magneto-chemistry*, Macmillan and Co., Ltd., London, 1935, pp. 283–288. Short discussions of several of the above effects. Pp. 299–300, miscellaneous effects; pp. 326–335, chemical reactions; pp. 350 for discussion of nematic type liquid crystals.

See also Galvanomagnetic and Thermomagnetic Effects, Magnetic Susceptance (Gauss Effect), Magnetostriction and Allied Effects.

* Consult index for further information.

Quantities

Current	Intensity	Light	Permeability
Direction	Length	Magnetic flux	Resistivity

MAGNETIC SUSCEPTANCE (GAUSS EFFECT)

I. Description

The resistance of metals increases if magnetized in the same direction as the current flow, and decreases if the magnetic field is transverse. The effect is proportional to the square of the field intensity.

II. Illustration

Bismuth wire coils using the Gauss effect have been used to explore variations in flux intensity for space as well as time coordinates.

III. Magnitude

Bismuth is one of the few metals which shows a usable susceptance or Gauss effect. This effect is shown by placing a strip of wire in a magnetic field and measuring the change in electrical resistance for different field intensities. This linear change of resistance with field strength (above 2000 gauss) for bismuth is diminished at low field values by the effect of temperature. This material also has a large Hall effect and is the most diamagnetic material known. For bismuth wire, resistance values are:

RELATIVE RESISTANCE (°C)

H (Gauss)	−192°	−37°	0°	18°	60°	100°
0	0.40	0.88	1.00	1.08	1.25	1.42
4,000	2.32	1.10	1.18	1.21	1.31	1.46
6,000	4.00	1.24	1.30	1.32	1.39	1.51
10,000	8.60	1.72	1.57	1.54	1.54	1.62
20,000	19.8	2.81	2.38	2.20	1.97	1.95
35,000	35.5	4.95	3.62	3.25	2.69	2.95

IV. References

1. Bozorth, *Ferromagnetism,* D. Van Nostrand Co., New York, 1951, p. 745.
2. Bhatmager, S. S., and K. N. Mathur, *Physical Principles and Applications of Magnetochemistry,* Macmillan and Co., Ltd., London, 1935, pp. 294–299. Discussion for solids and liquids.
3. Campbell, L. L., *Galvanomagnetic and Thermomagnetic Effects,* Longmans, Green and Co., New York, 1923, pp. 158–208. Various materials and effect of field.

See also Galvanomagnetic and Thermomagnetic Effects, Magnetostriction and Allied Effects, Magnetic Effects.

Quantities

Magnetic flux   Resistivity   Temperature

MAGNETOSTRICTION AND ALLIED EFFECTS

(Joule, Villari, Wertheim, and Wiedemann effects)

I. Description

The term magnetostriction refers to the change in dimensions of a ferromagnetic material when it is placed in a magnetic field. It also applies to the inverse effect, that is, the change in magnetization when the dimensions are changed by an external force.

Magnetostriction is exhibited by the ferromagnetic metals, iron, nickel and cobalt, and most alloys of these three. The lesser known ferromagnetic Heusler alloys (containing copper, manganese, and tin originally) and gadolinium also are magnetostrictive.

Magnetostriction effects are classified as follows:

Joule effect

The Joule effect deals with the change in length of a ferromagnetic material along the axis of the applied magnetic field when this field is changed. For most purposes the longitudinal change is important, but it should be noted that a volume and transverse change also occurs. The volume change is the basis of the low expansion alloys to be described later.

Villari effect

The Villari effect relates to the fact that the magnetization of a material, in the presence of a field, is altered upon the application of external stress.

Villari reversal

In pure iron, under conditions of high field strength, the magnetostriction effect changes sign, i.e., the direction of dimensional change reverses.

Wertheim effect

When a wire, placed in a longitudinal magnetic field is being twisted, there is a transient voltage difference between the ends of the wire.

Wiedemann effect

The direct Wiedemann effect is the twist produced in a wire, placed in a longitudinal magnetic field, when a current flows through the wire. This is due to the helical resultant of the impressed longitudinal field and the circular field of the wire. The magnetic material expands (or contracts) parallel to the helical lines of force and hence the twist. The inverse Wiedemann effect is the axial magnetization of a current-carrying wire, when twisted.

Allied effects

1. Change in electrical resistance due to field (Gauss effect).
2. Change in thermoelectrical emf due to field (Nerst effect).
3. Emf due to magnetization (Faraday's law of induction).
4. Change in frequency of tuning fork due to a field.
5. Sounds produced by magnetization.

Factors that control the effects are: (1) heat treatment, (2) stress, (3) hardness, (4) impurities, and (5) previous magnetic history.

II. Illustration

Since 1926 when it was classed as a laboratory curiosity, magnetostrictive effects have found use in the following diverse commercial fields:

1. Sonar and related devices for detecting submarines and ships.
2. The fathometer used to determine the depths of uncharted waters. Post war use of this device has been to locate schools of fish.
3. Electrical filters; in particular, a band pass filter for use in commercial receiving sets.
4. Homogenization and sterilization of milk.
5. Acceleration of chemical reactions and cavitation effects. Ultrasonic soldering iron.
6. Strain gages.
7. Vibration and engine detonation.
8. Phonograph pickups.
9. Frequency control of oscillators operating below 100,000 cycles.
10. Dust precipitation.

III. Magnitude

At this point it would be wise to dispel two popular misconceptions concerning magnetostriction. The first is that large changes in length take place. Actually, in nickel, which shows one of the largest changes per unit length of all the materials investigated, this amounts to about 30 parts in one million. For a nickel rod 1 foot long, this would amount to 3.6 ten thousandths of an inch. At resonance this change may be as high as one part in a thousand (limited by fatigue properties), or a rod 1 foot long changes about one hundreth of an inch.

The other popular misconception is that a rod, constrained at each end and subjected to a magnetic field, will exert an infinite force in attempting to contract. Actually, the static force is determined by change in length and the modulus of elasticity of the metal. For nickel the maximum static force is about 1000 psi, while the force for iron or cobalt is lower.

Joule effect

The Joule effect can be determined within an accuracy of 4 to 5% with iron.

Iron-carbon alloy

$H = 1800$ gauss

$$\frac{L - L_0}{L_0} = -7.53 \times 10^{-6}$$

Iron-cobalt alloy

$H = 550$ gauss

$$\frac{L - L_0}{L_0} = 64.67 \times 10^{-6}$$

where L = sample length

L_0 = sample length with magnetic field applied

Wiedemann effect

The Wiedemann effect can be determined with higher precision. For a circular cylinder, bar or tube in a longitudinal field of 75 gauss and a current of 8.86 amp, the twist was 0.954 sec of angular deflection per cm of length.

For a low carbon steel tube where

$$D_0 = 0.16 \text{ cm} \qquad D_1 = 0.0794 \text{ cm} \qquad L = 79.8 \text{ cm}$$

$$H = 30 \text{ gauss} \qquad I = 1.5 \text{ amp}$$

the deflection was 5.226 minutes per cm of length.

IV. References

1. Bozorth, R. M., *Ferromagnetism,* D. Van Nostrand Co., 1951, p. 628.
2. Koboyasi, T., "On the Inverse Wiedemann Effect and Allied Phenomena," *Japanese Journal of Physics Transactions,* No. 1, Vol. 5, pp. 116–139, and No. 3, Vol. 5, pp. 111–117.
3. Bradfield, G., "A New Electro-Acoustical Transducer," *Electronic Engineering,* March, 1948, Vol. 20, No. 241, pp. 74–78. A pulse generator and receiver using magnetostriction.
4. *Magnetostriction.* A pamphlet published by Development and Research Division, The International Nickel Co., New York, February, 1952.

See also Galvanomagnetic and Thermomagnetic Effects, Magnetic Effects, Magnetic Susceptance (Gauss Effect).

Quantities

Amplitude	Current	Length	Sound
Angle	Force	Magnetic flux	Stress
Coefficient of expansion	Frequency	Permeability	Temperature

MEMORY METALS

I. Description

Certain single crystal alloys, if deformed soon after their formation, will revert to their original shape when heated to their transformation temperature.

II. Illustration

An alloy of gold and cadmium with 47.5 ± 1 atomic percent cadmium and the remainder gold may be made into a single crystal of cubic structure. As the crystal cools below 60°C, several domains of orthorhombic structure form within the cubic structure of the crystal. This is a regular first-order phase change. Now, the crystal may be bent and given a permanent set. After a period of time on the shelf or after an anneal of 50°C, the crystal will exhibit a pseudoelastic behavior (hence, the permanent set must be made soon after the transformation). If, at any time, the crystal is heated to about 75°C, the transformation which the crystal experienced upon cooling will be reversed. The orthorhombic domains will change back and must fit themselves into the original cubic structure. The crystal reverts to the original shape it had before bending.

III. Magnitude

A Au-Cd crystal 2 inches long may be given a 45° bend. When heated to 75°C, it will exert a force of several pounds if restrained from returning to its original shape. The effect is also observed in alloys of indium and thallium with 21 ± 2 atomic percent thallium. The transformation temperature is about 70°C.

IV References

1. Chang, Lo-ching, "Coefficients of Thermal Expansion of AuCd Alloys Containing 47.5 Atomic Percent Cd," *Journal of Applied Physics,* April, 1951, Vol. 22, No. 4, pp. 525 and 526.
2. Read, T. A., and L. C. Chang, "AuCd Alloy," *Journal of Metals,* Japan, 1951, p. 47, p. 191.
3. Burkhardt, M. W., "Indium Thallium Alloy," *Journal of Metals,* November, 1953. (Paper for Columbia University Master's Thesis, given at AIME Meeting at Cleveland, October, 1953.)
4. Chang, L. C., *Journal of Applied Physics,* 1952, Vol. 23, p. 727.

Quantities

Force	Length	Stress
Heat flux	Strain	Temperature

NEWTON'S LAW OF HEATING AND COOLING
(Also known as convection heat transfer)

I. Description

Newton's law of heating and cooling states that a temperature difference between an object and a fluid in contact causes heat to flow. This is the idealized case of convective heat transfer.

II. Illustration

Consider an object being heated from some initial uniform temperature state. If the object is of high thermal conductivity, then its internal thermal resistance can be ignored, and we can regard the heat transfer process as being controlled by the surface resistance or film coefficient.

The solution to problems of this type where the simplest conditions of Newtonian heating or cooling exist demonstrates an exponential rise or fall in temperature of the object.

III. Magnitude

The rate of heat gained or lost to the surroundings by an object is given by:

$$q = CwV \frac{dt}{d\theta} = hA(t_f - t)$$

where q = heat flux
C = thermal capacity
w = specific weight
V = total volume
A = surface area
t = object's uniform temperature at instant θ
h = unit surface conductance
t_f = fluid temperature
θ = time

Empirical relations have been determined for many configurations. For instance, the heat transfer coefficient between horizontal plates and still air under free convection is given by Reference 1 as

$$h = 0.38 \ (t_f - t)^{0.25} \qquad \text{Btu hr}^{-1} \text{ ft}^{-2} \text{ F}^{-1}$$

for plates facing upward, and

$$h = 0.2 \ (t_f - t)^{0.25} \qquad \text{Btu hr}^{-1} \text{ ft}^{-2} \text{ F}^{-1}$$

for plates facing downward.

IV. References

1. Jakob, M., and G. Hawkins, *Elements of Heat Transfer*, 3rd Ed., John Wiley and Sons, New York, 1957. Elementary introduction to convection heat transfer.
2. McAdams, W. H., *Heat Transmission*, McGraw-Hill Book Co., 1942. General empirical coverage of convection heat transfer.
3. Schneider, P. J., *Conduction Heat Transfer*, Addison-Wesley Publishing Co., Cambridge, Mass., 1955, p. 360. A brief presentation.

Quantities

Area	Film coefficient	Mass	Temperature
Conductivity	Heat flux	Specific heat	Volume

NEWTON'S LAWS

●

I. Description

First Law. A body at rest remains at rest, and a body in uniform motion continues in a straight line unless the body is acted upon by an unbalanced force.

Second Law. A body accelerates in proportion to and in the same direction as the unbalanced force acting upon it.

Third Law. For every action there is an equal and opposite reaction.

II. Illustration

A combination of the first and second laws allows a description of planetary motions. (See Kepler's law.)

The third law is basic to a number of fields. Examples are Lenz's law, Hooke's law, Gibbs theory of equilibria, and the Peltier effect.

III. Magnitude

The formula covering these three laws is:

$$F = ma$$

where F = force (unbalanced on the mass)

m = mass

a = acceleration of the mass

This formula is used to define the units of various systems of measures. Some consistent sets are listed below:

F	m	a	
poundal	pound	ft/sec²	British absolute
pound	slugs	ft/sec²	British gravitational
dyne	gram	cm/sec²	Metric absolute
gram	gram/cm/sec²	cm/sec²	Metric gravitational

The formula has been modified somewhat by relativistic concepts, but it is still used whenever the velocity of the mass does not exceed one-tenth the speed of light.

D'Alembert's principle uses the third law (and the formula) to allow a force balance in dynamic situations with accelerating particles.

IV. Reference

1. Campbell, J. W., *An Introduction to Mechanics,* Houghton, Mifflin Co., Boston, 1947. Laws, problems. D'Alembert's principle, illustrations, problems.

Quantities

Acceleration   Direction   Force   Mass   Velocity

OHM'S LAW

I. Description

The current through impedance will be proportional to the electromotive force across the impedance.

II. Illustration

Inserting a resistance in series with a current reading meter will change it to a device for indicating voltage. The voltage range is dependent on the current range of the meter, and the value of the series resistance. At high current densities there are slight deviations from the law that are due to nonuniform current flow. Similar deviations occur that are due to distributed circuit constants on alternating current.

III. Magnitude

Ohm's law is most often stated:

$$I = \frac{E}{R}$$

where I = current
E = emf of cell
R = resistance of circuit

For alternating currents, R is replaced by:

$$Z = \sqrt{R^2 + \left(\omega L - \frac{1}{\omega C}\right)^2}$$

where Z = impedance (ohms)
ω = $2\pi f$
f = frequency in cps
L = inductance in henrys
C = capacity in farads

If the total resistance of a series resistance and instrument coil is 10,000 ohms, with an instrument designed to measure one milliampere for full-scale deflection, the meter would now read ten volts for full-scale deflection.

IV. References

1. Timbie, W. H., and V. Bush, *Principles of Electrical Engineering,* John Wiley and Sons, New York, 4th Ed., 1951.
2. Hausman, E., and E. Slack, *Physics,* D. Van Nostrand Co., New York, 1948, pp. 378–380. A short statement of the law with illustrative problems.

See also Skin Effect, Wein Effect.

Quantities

Capacitance	Frequency	Potential
Current	Inductance	Resistivity

OPTICAL ROTARY POWER

I. Description

Certain optically transparent materials cause the plane of polarization of light passing through the material to rotate. The materials which exhibit this property may be solids, liquids, or vapors. The rotation may be either dextrorotary (CW) or levorotary (CCW) depending upon the material and wavelength. The angle through which the plane rotates is directly proportional to the length of path, the physical properties of the material, and inversely proportional to the wavelength squared of the incident light (Biot's law).

The specific rotation of a given soluble compound is defined as the angle of rotation through which the plane of polarized light is turned in passing through a tube 1 decimeter long, filled with a solution containing 1 gram of the substance per 1000 cc. Both temperature and source of light must be specified. Generally 20°C is specified using the sodium D line.

II. Illustration

The concentration of a solution can be monitored by measuring the angle of rotation of plane polarized light passing through a given distance of the solution.

The saccharimeter is a special type of polarimeter used to analyze sugars. Dextrose is a simple sugar which rotates the plane of polarization to the right (CW).

Molecular structures of chemical compounds are studied and analyzed by their inherent optical rotary properties.

III. Magnitude

For several materials, the rotary powers are:

Material	Rotation	(°/mm)
Quartz	21.68	at 5890 A (sodium)
Crystalline sucrose (table sugar)	235.97	at 2143 A (cadmium)
Crystalline sucrose (table sugar)	54.0	(Sodium D)
Sucrose solution specific rotation	0.66	(Sodium D)
Turpentine	0.37	(Sodium D)

A long column of vapor has the same rotary power as the short column of liquid into which it condenses, cross section remaining equal (Beer's or Lambert's law).

IV. References

1. Hodgman, Charles D., *Handbook of Chemistry and Physics,* Chemical Rubber Publishing Co., Cleveland, Ohio, 1955. Tables for various solutions.
2. MacDougall, Frank H., *Physical Chemistry,* The Macmillan Co., New York, 1952, pp. 205–207. Cause and measurement.
3. Preston, Thomas, *The Theory of Light,* Macmillan and Co., Ltd., London, 1929, p. 427. Qualitative discussion.

Quantities

Angle	Concentration	Length	Polarization
Chemical composition	Frequency	Light	

ORGAN PIPE RESONANCE

I. Description

A closed or open pipe filled with gas will produce vibrations in the gas at specific frequencies depending on the pipe length.

II. Illustration

A Kundt tube demonstrates organ pipe resonance and may be used to measure the velocity of sound in a gas by tuning a horizontal column of gas to resonance. Lycopodium or similar powder in the tube then collects at the nodes. The velocity of sound in the gas is:

$$v = 2fd$$

where v = velocity of sound in the gas
f = frequency
d = distance between nodes

III. Magnitude

For a closed pipe or other air column of length L where V is the velocity of sound in air, the frequencies of vibration for the fundamental and the first three overtones are:

$$F_0 = \frac{V}{4L} \qquad F_1 = \frac{3V}{4L} \qquad F_2 = \frac{5V}{4L} \qquad F_3 = \frac{7V}{4L}$$

For an open pipe:

$$F_0 = \frac{V}{2L} \qquad F_1 = \frac{2V}{2L} \qquad F_2 = \frac{3V}{2L} \qquad F_3 = \frac{4V}{2L}$$

Orifices may also be used to produce tones. For a rectangular opening of width d, the jet tone produced has a frequency f of:

$$f = 0.044 \frac{v}{d} \text{ for air}$$

$$f = 0.046 \frac{v}{d} \text{ for water}$$

where v is the velocity of the fluid.

The jet tone is somewhat more productive of overtones (noise) than the resonant organ pipe. The intensity of the sound is limited by the energy supplied.

IV. References

1. Hausmann, E., and E. Slack, *Physics,* D. Van Nostrand Co., New York, 1948, pp. 583–584. Simple tube formulas.
2. Anderson, A. B. C., "A Circular Orifice Number Describing Dependency of Primary Pfeifenton Frequency on Differential Pressure, Gas Density and Orifice Geometry," *The Journal of the Acoustical Society of America,* Vol. 25, No. 4, July, 1953, pp. 626–631. Tones generated by orifices.

Quantities

Frequency Gas Length Resonance Sound

PASCHEN'S LAW

I. Description

The sparking potential between two terminals in a given gas is a function of the product of the pressure and the spark length, i.e., upon the mass of gas between a unit area of the electrodes.

II. Illustration

For any given distance between electrodes in a gas, there is some critical pressure at which discharge occurs at the minimum sparking potential of the gas. Thus with a gap 3 mm in air, sparkover occurs at a pressure of 1.5 mm at about 340 volts. For a gap of 1 mm the discharge occurs at a pressure of 5 mm at the same voltage. At pressures above and below these minima, or critical pressures, the voltage necessary to produce a breakdown of the gas increases with both increasing and decreasing pressures. This effect is important for internal combustion engines.

III. Magnitude

Paschen's law may be written:

$$V = f(p,d)$$

where p = pressure of gas
$\quad\quad d$ = spark length

It has been shown that Paschen's law holds for all pressures. These results are very important in that to find the sparking potential corresponding to any spark length and any pressure, it is only necessary to know the results of experiments made with a constant spark length over the whole range of pressures.

In all cases, the dimensions of the electrodes should be very large compared with the distance between them.

Gas	Minimum Spark Potential	P × d in mm × mm
Air	341	5.7
N_2	251	6.7
H_2	278	14.4
O_2	455	

IV. References

1. Crowther, James Arnold, *Ions, Electrons and Ionizing Radiation,* Cambridge University Press, London, 1949. Short derivation of the law.
2. Boyle, W. S., and P. Kisliak, "Departure from Paschen's Law of Breakdown in Gases," *Physical Review* Vol. 97., No. 2., Jan.

15, 1955, pp. 255–259. An explanation of the departures from the law at small spacings and high pressures.

Quantities

Chemical composition   Gas   Length   Potential   Pressure

PERIODIC LAW (OR TABLE)

I. Description

If the elements are arranged in order of atomic number (number of electrons), a periodic repetition of their chemical and physical properties is apparent.

II. Illustration

Group I contains hydrogen, lithium, sodium, potassium, rubidium, and cesium in order of increasing atomic weights. All of these materials display a valence of +1 (similar chemical behavior) and are very active chemically. Likewise the inert gases, helium, neon, argon, krypton, and xenon occupy similar positions. Physical properties are also similar as given by the photoelectric effect (alkali metals) and electrical conductivity (silver, copper).

III. Magnitude

The arrangement of the elements will give only qualitative results regarding behavior. Chemical reactivity is associated primarily, however, with the outermost electrons in an atom, and does not depend on electrons in shells below the surface.

IV. References

1. MacDougall, Frank H., *Physical Chemistry,* The Macmillan Co., New York, 1952, pp. 155–158. Usefulness and limits of periodic table.
2. Tomaschek, *Grimsehls Oehrbuch der Physik,* B. G. Teubner in Leipzig and Berlin, 1934. P. 6, periodicity of atom diameter; p. 7, periodicity of melting point.

Quantities

Chemical composition   Radiation

PHOTOELECTRIC EFFECTS

I. Description

There are three types of photoelectric effects:

1. *Photoemissive effect*—emission of electrons from metallic surfaces when radiation impinges upon the surface.

2. *Photovoltaic effect*—generation of a voltage across the boundary between two metals when radiation strikes this boundary.

3. *Photoconductive effect*—change in resistance of a semi-conductor as a result of incident radiation.

Historically these effects appear with various names. Hertz, as well as Wiedemann and Ebert, found that illuminating the cathode of a gap will facilitate the sparking, the action occurring at the cathode.

Elster and Geitel found (as did Hertz) that negatively charged substances lose their charge when illuminated by ultraviolet, or bodies initially uncharged gain a positive potential under this light.

II. Illustration

The light meter uses a photovoltaic cell as a source of current to drive a d-c meter. Deflection of the meter is proportional to the light flux falling on the face of the cell.

The photoemissive type cell is generally used in the sound system of motion picture machines. Density variations of the sound strip on the film produce variations in the amount of light striking the cell. This causes a signal to be generated which is amplified and converted to sound.

The photoconductive type cell is not yet in common use. Selenium and germanium are often used in this type of cell, which is starting to find applications.

III. Magnitude

All these effects follow Einstein's (or Millikan's) photoelectric equation:

$$hf = w + \left[\frac{\frac{1}{2}m_0v^2}{\sqrt{1 - \left(\frac{v}{c}\right)^2}} \right]$$

where m_0 = rest mass of electron
h = Planck's constant
f = frequency of incident radiation
w = work function of the emitter
v = velocity of electron
c = velocity of light

Since the work function is the energy required to move an electron away from the surface of the emitter, it is seen that there is a lower frequency limit below which no electrons will be emitted and thus no photoelectric effect will be observed. Above this critical level the frequency response depends upon the construction of the cell.

Photoemissive type cells have a sensitivity of up to 500 volts per lumen of light incident to the cell surface. Gas-filled phototubes have about double this value. While the current is generally proportional to the illumination for intensity ranges of 50,000 to 1, this linearity does not hold for polarized light.

The photovoltaic cell has an output of about 500 microamperes per lumen with a very low resistance load. The voltage output is low, the maximum being about 0.4 millivolt per lumen. The efficiencies of some semi-conductor photovoltaic cells approaches 10%, although the voltage per cell is still low. The resistance of the photoconductive type cell is between 0.1 to 25 megohms and can vary as much as 25 to 1 from its no light to maximum light condition. The current range is below 500 milliamperes. Modern semi-conductor cells may lower the resistance and range of saturated to dark current ratios to 100 to 1. Semi-conductor cells tend to be temperature sensitive. For some metals like platinum, the energy required to pull an electron away from the surface is large, whereas for other metals like the alkalies or chemical compounds, it is quite small; W, the work function varies:

	Work Function, electron volts
Cesium	1.81
Lithium	2.36
Molybdenum	4.15
Platinum	6.27
Potassium	1.77
Tungsten	4.54
Strontium oxide	1.27

The more electropositive the metal in the contact potential series, the longer the wavelength to which it will respond photoelectrically.

IV. References

1. Richtmyer, F. R., and E. H. Kennard, *Introduction to Modern Physics*, McGraw-Hill Book Co., 1955. A general discussion with equations.

See also The Hertz Effect.

Quantities

Chemical composition	Frequency Intensity	Light Polarization	Potential Speed of light

Energy (K.E.)

PHOTOMAGNETIC EFFECT

I. Description

Some salts show a slight increase in their paramagnetic behavior after exposure to light.

II. Illustration

The paramagnetic behavior is observable for chromic chloride.

One type of Hall effect near absolute zero generates a voltage in cuprous oxide perpendicular to both the mutually perpendicular incident white light and magnetic field.

III. Magnitude

There is some question as to whether the paramagnetic effect exists, as its magnitude is relatively small. The photomagnetic Hall effect produces a voltage as a linear function of the field up to 2500 gauss, the voltage there being 2.7 volts.

IV. Reference

1. Bhatnagar, S. S. and K. N. Mathur, *Physical Principles and Applications of Magneto-chemistry,* Macmillan and Co., Ltd., London, 1935, pp. 279–280. A presentation of the conflicting evidence; p. 292, the photomagnetic Hall effect.

See also Hall Effect.

Quantities

Light   Magnetic flux   Potential   Radiation

PIEZOELECTRIC EFFECT

I. Description

Certain crystals become electrified when subjected to compression or tension. The electric charges developed on the faces of the crystal are proportional to the pressure. This is particularly useful in measuring high frequency pressures or steep wave-front transients, where ordinary devices would have too much inertia.

Electrostriction is the converse; an electric field alters the shape of such a crystal. If an alternating electric field applied to such a crystal has a frequency near the natural mechanical frequency of the crystal, these mechanical vibrations become very large. Most dielectrics demonstrate electrostriction, but not piezoelectricity.

There is a related ferroelectric effect where certain materials such as Rochelle salts exhibit a dielectric hysteresis and possess a Curie point. (See Curie-Weiss Law.)

In addition, two second-order effects have recently become important. These are the electro-optical and the piezo-optical effects which are caused respectively by the change in dielectric constant due to an applied voltage and the change in dielectric constant due to an applied stress.

II. Illustration

A crystal placed in the grid circuit of a vacuum tube oscillator serves as an excellent source of frequency stabilization. This serves as a source of frequency stabilization and this method is almost always used for radio transmitters. This effect is also used in ultrasonic transducers, microphones, phonograph pickups, and earphones.

The electro-optical effect has been prepared for use as a variable band pass filter, the position of which band can be controlled by an applied voltage.

III. Magnitude

A. The Q of such crystal oscillators varies from a few thousand to as high as 500,000.

B. The following is piezoelectric data on barium titanate:
Conversion of mechanical energy to electrical energy—25 to 40%.
Conversion constant—150×10^{-12} coulomb/newton.

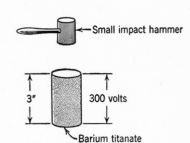

The following demonstrative setup yielded an output voltage pulse of 300 volts peak.

IV. References

1. Wooster, W. A., *A Text-Book on Crystal Physics*, Cambridge University Press, London, 1949, pp. 188–222. Theory, testing, and uses.
2. Bazhenov, V. A., *Trud. Inst., Lesa,* 1953, vol. 9, pp. 281–314, Referativnyi Zh., Fiz k, pp. 172–173, March, 1955, Abstract 4950.
3. *Proceedings of IRE,* October, 1955, Vol. 43, No. 10, p. 1562. Effect in wood about one-tenth for quartz.
4. Mason, W. P., *Piezoelectric Crystals and Their Application to Ultrasonics,* D. Van Nostrand Co., New York, 1950. A complete treatment of this effect using advanced mathematics.

See also Ferroelectric Phenomena.

Quantities

Charge   Force   Frequency   Potential   Strain

PINCH EFFECT

I. Description

The passage of an electric current through a liquid conductor tends to reduce the cross section of the conductor. This effect can be explained by considering that an infinite number of parallel conductors, carrying current in the same direction, will attract each other. This force will tend to reduce the conductor area.

II. Illustration

This effect is noticeable when high conductivity metals are heated in an induction furnace of the type where the metal forms the secondary turn on the transformer. To be liquefied, these metals require very high current densities at the part of the channel that presents the smallest initial cross section, hence the force of contraction will then be the greatest. As the cross section reduces, the force progressively increases so that the metal may even be severed. The observed effect will be a rapid opening and closing of a gap in the fluid. The resultant decreases in average current usually allow the metal to freeze.

This effect might be put to use as a current-limiting device using mercury in a small tube.

III. Magnitude

The pressure, P, at the center of conductor of circular cross section due to the pinch effect is given by:

$$P = \frac{I^2}{100S} \text{ dynes/cm}^2$$

where I = current, amp

S = cross-sectional area, square cm

The table below gives the maximum currents that can be passed through liquid iron in channels of three sizes.

Depth, inches	Width, inches	Current, amperes
2	1	3,300
4	2	9,400
6	3	17,000

IV. References

1. Thompson, M. D. K., *Theoretical and Applied Electrochemistry*, The Macmillan Co., New York, 1939.
2. Liddell, D. M., *Handbook of Non-Ferrous Metallurgy*, McGraw-Hill Book Co., New York, 1945.
3. Koehler, W. A., *Principles and Applications of Electrochemistry*, John Wiley and Sons, New York, 2nd Ed., 1944, Vol. 2, p. 424.

Quantities

Area   Current   Force   Magnetic flux   Pressure

POISSON'S COEFFICIENT (OR RATIO)

I. Description

The longitudinal stretching of any elastic material is accompanied by a lateral contraction, and the ratio of the contraction to the proportional stretching is known as Poisson's coefficient.

II. Illustration

For materials in which there is no grain to elasticity, the value of Poisson's ratio was demonstrated by that celebrated mathematician to be 0.25, and actual cases bear out his deductions closely. For most metals it lies between 0.25 and 0.33. If the volume remained constant, M would be 0.50; therefore the volume of most metals increases slightly when loaded in uniaxial tension and decreases when loaded in uniaxial compression.

III. Magnitude

The proportional stretching or unit (elongation per unit of length) is the strain in the material and may be denoted by S. Calling Poisson's coefficient M:

$$\text{lateral contraction} = M \times S$$

hence lateral dimensions diminish by a percentage equal to 100 MS. For some common materials, Poisson's ratio is:

Steel	0.278–0.305
Cast iron	0.211–0.299
Copper	0.355
Brass	0.331
Aluminum alloys	0.330–0.334

The shear modulus G, Poisson's ratio and Young's modulus E are related:

$$G = \frac{E}{2(1 + M)}$$

IV. References

1. Young, J. F., *Materials and Processes,* John Wiley and Sons, New York, 2nd Ed., 1954, p. 92. Short definition.
2. Timoshenko, S., and J. N. Goodier, *Theory of Elasticity,* McGraw-Hill Book Co., New York, 1951, pp. 254–5. Method of determining ratio by the use of beams.
3. Hetényi, M. I., *Handbook of Experimental Stress Analysis,* John Wiley and Sons, New York, 1950, pp. 767–770. Poisson's ratio in dealing with scale models.

Quantities

Force   Length   Strain   Volume

PROXIMITY EFFECT

I. Description

When a wire is carrying an alternating current, or, in general, any current whose magnitude is varying, the current has a tendency to crowd toward one side of a conductor owing to the proximity of another current-carrying conductor. This effect increases the resistance much the same as the skin effect. The effect on inductance is practically negligible when the spacing between wires is large compared to the diameter of the wire.

II. Illustration

This effect can cause unequal heating of large bus bars carrying heavy currents when such a bar is located near another conductor.

III. Magnitude

The effective resistance of the line, R_{eff}, is given by:

$$R_{eff} = \frac{134F \times \sqrt{f} \times 10^{-4} \text{ ohms/mile}}{r}$$

where f = frequency in cps.

r = radius of the wire in cm

d = distance between the centers of the wires in cm

F = experimental proximity factor, F versus $(d - r)/r$:

$(d - r)/r$	F
4	1.15
6	1.06
8	1.037
12	1.02
16	1.01
20	1.002
32	1.00

IV. Reference

1. Ware, L. A., and H. R. Reed, *Communication Circuits*, John Wiley and Sons, New York, 3rd Ed., 1949.

Quantities

Current   Frequency   Length   Resistivity

PURKINJE EFFECT

I. Description

The human eye is less sensitive to light of longer wavelengths under conditions of decreased illumination.

II. Illustration

This effect complicates visual determination of celestial magnitudes of different colored stars. It is a source of difficulty in the manufacture of color photography emulsions due to the varying degrees of contrast required for different wavelengths.

Violet and blue lights can be detected at greater distances by a dark-adapted eye than red lights. Blackout filters are red, not blue or green, to reduce possibility of light detection by the enemy.

Dark adaption occurs in the short wave range of the spectrum. Red goggles are worn so that the eyes may dark-adapt while still in use for map reading or briefing prior to night operations.

This effect may be useful in displays and advertising. Tail lights should be half-violet and half-red for best day and night usefulness.

Relative visibility colors can be selected for clothing, paint, lights, etc., depending on day or night use.

III. Magnitude

Red, orange, and yellow appear brightest under moderate illumination. A red (670 mu*) may be 10 times brighter to a light-adapted eye than a blue (480 mu). Decreasing light intensity to 1 lumen/sq ft begins a sensitivity shift into the greens. At 0.1 lumen/sq ft, a dark-adapted eye sees the blue 16 times brighter than the red.

IV. References

1. Jacobs, Donald H., *Fundamentals of Optical Engineering*, Mc-Graw-Hill Book Co., New York, 1943, pp. 81–84. Law and related effects.
2. Luckiesh, Matthew, and Frank K. Moss, *The Science of Seeing*, D. Van Nostrand Co., New York, 1937, pp. 62, 66–71. Dark adaptation.

Quantities

Color   Intensity   Light

PYROELECTRIC EFFECT

I. Description

Charges appear at the ends of certain crystals when their temperature is changed. The polarity of these charges reverses when the direction of temperature change is reversed.

* 1 mu = 10^{-7} cm.

II. Illustration

A very small crystal could be used to measure transient temperature effects, and the voltage so developed could be used to operate an a-c electronic amplifier. Temperature differences in quartz produce charges, but this is a piezoelectric effect. Crystals which exhibit pyroelectricity are cane sugar, calamine, boracite, pentalrythrital, lithiumsulfatmonohydrate, and some kinds of topaz.

III. Magnitude

The induced potential is proportional to the temperature change, not the rate of change. Tourmaline crystals develop 300 volts per cm for each °C. The actual charge, however, is very small.

IV. References

1. Wooster, W. A., *A Text-Book on Crystal Physics,* University Press, Cambridge, England, 1949, pp. 223–230. Quantitative description and discussion.
2. Hayden, J. L. R., and Steinmetz, "Insulation, Failure—a Pyroelectric Effect," *Electrical World,* Vol. 80, 1922, p. 865.

Quantities

Charge   Potential   Temperature

QUANTUM THEORY

I. Description

This law states that radiation is emitted in discrete bunches or quanta.

II. Illustration

All electromagnetic waves, including radio, follow this law. This theory is also the basis for the explanation of the photoelectric effect. It is of importance in luminescence and phosphorescence.

III. Magnitude

The various electrons in an atom occupy discrete energy positions. It is only when the electrons transfer from one position to the other that a quanta of energy is liberated. The energy state is defined by quantum number, four being required to describe the state of any electron. Pauli's exclusion principle states that only one electron in the atom may occupy a quantum state. The individual quanta have an energy of

$$E = \hbar f$$

where $\hbar = 6.67 \times 10^{-27}$ erg second (Planck's constant)
  f = frequency of radiation

Using the quantum idea as a basis, the Planck radiation law was derived which expresses the radiation intensity of a given wavelength. Approximately:

$$\psi_\lambda = \frac{8\pi c \hbar}{\lambda^5 (e^{ch/\lambda kT} - 1)}$$

where ψ_λ = radiation intensity at one wavelength
  k = Boltzmann constant 1.381×10^{-16} erg/degree
  $\hbar$ = Planck's constant

T = absolute temperature degrees Kelvin
λ = wavelength in cm
c = velocity of light 2.9978×10^{10} cm/sec

IV. References

1. Richtmyer, F. K., E. H. Kennard, and T. Lauritsen, *Introduction to Modern Physics*, McGraw-Hill Book Co., New York, 1955. Pp. 130–132, derivation; see also pp. 172–223 for wave mechanics.
See also Photoelectric Effect, Stokes's Law of Fluorescence.

Quantities

Energy (K.E.)   Frequency   Radiation   Speed of Light   Temperature

RADIATION PRESSURE

I. Description

Electromagnetic waves carry momentum; they can thus be expected to exert a pressure on surfaces upon which they impinge.

II. Illustration

It probably should be pointed out that the radiometer does *not* operate because of radiation pressure, but in spite of it. The curvature of comet's tails is due to this cause, however.

III. Magnitude

For an absorbing surface, radiation pressure is:

$$p = \frac{nI}{c} \quad \text{or}$$

$$p = w \cos^2 \theta$$

where p = dynes per cm^2
n = refractive index of medium or c/v
I = intensity of radiation
c = velocity of light in free space
v = velocity of propagation in medium
w = energy density of the radiation
θ = angle of radiation from normal to surface

The force is small, being about 2×10^{-5} dyne per cm^2 for sunlight.

IV. Reference

1. Richtmyer, F. K., E. H. Kennard, and T. Lauritsen, *Introduction to Modern Physics*, McGraw-Hill Book Co., New York, 1955. Derivation of the formula.

Quantities

Light   Pressure   Radiation   Speed of light

RADIOACTIVITY

I. Description

The nuclei of some materials may be either naturally or artificially unstable, emitting, with time, helium nuclei (alpha particles), electrons (beta rays), or gamma rays (X-rays), and by this process the material changes to a new element.

II. Illustration

Alpha or beta rays are utilized in some low-power but long-life batteries for such items as wrist watches. Beta rays are also used to gage foil thickness. Both are also used as deionizing sources for static electricity control in paper, plastic, and textile mills.

Gamma rays are used to examine castings for flaws in the same manner as are X-rays. They have also been employed to examine strata in oil prospecting. While they are also used for sheet-metal thickness gaging in rolling mills, their use is limited by the precautions necessary to protect operating personnel. These precautions often cost more than the functional cost of the equipment.

III. Magnitude

There is a constant probability that each atom will break down, thus the speed of the radioactive disintegration is proportional to the number present, or

$$\frac{dN_\epsilon}{dt} = -\lambda N_\epsilon$$

where N_ϵ = number of atoms present
λ = a constant
t = time

The half-life of a material is the time required for one-half of the atoms initially present to break down. The half-life of the material is unaffected by heat or pressure.

The alpha particles are powerful ionizers but poor penetrators. While they have a range proportional to the third power of their initial velocity, they travel only 3 to 9 cm in air but are stopped by a sheet of paper or 0.1 mm aluminum foil. Detection of alpha particles is by special counting screens.

The beta particles are electrons having a mass of 1/1845 that of a hydrogen atom and travel at an initial velocity of 33 to 99% the speed of light. Because of their low mass, their paths are very erratic as every collision bounces them in a new direction. They will penetrate several feet of air and up to 5 mm of aluminum. Detection may be by Geiger counters with special thin windows.

The gamma rays are the most powerful, passing through a foot of iron. They produce photographic effects, luminescence, and ionization as they are "hard" X-rays. These rays may interact with atomic nuclei and change direction without energy transfer. They may impart all or part of their energy to electrons, causing them to be expelled from their parent atoms with sufficient energy to produce many more ions. If they possess sufficiently high energy (16.18×10^{-14} joule), the quantum may be transformed into an electron and a positron, destroying energy but creating matter. These rays may be readily detected with Geiger counters.

The logarithmic graph below illustrates the wavelengths for gamma rays.

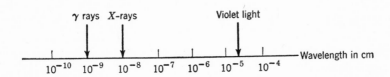

IV. References

1. Goodman, Clark, *The Science and Engineering of Nuclear Power*, Vol. 1, Addison-Wesley Publishing Co., Cambridge, Mass., 1952.

2. Halliday, David, *Introductory Nuclear Physics*, John Wiley and Sons, New York, 2nd Ed., 1955.

3. Richtmeyer, F. K., and E. H. Kennard, *Introduction to Modern Physics*, McGraw-Hill Book Co., New York, 1955. History and characteristics of radioactivity.

4. Glasstone, Samuel, *Sourcebook on Atomic Energy*, D. Van

Nostrand Co., New York, 1950, pp. 50–55. Discussion of several phases. Pp. 109–129, natural radioactivity.
Also see Group Displacement Law, Fission, Geiger-Nuttal Rule.

Quantities

Charge   Emissivity   Energy (K.E.)   Radiation

RAOULT'S LAW
(Includes Babo's law)

I. Description

According to Babo's law, the vapor pressure of a solvent is lowered on dissolving the solute. This lowering of vapor pressure for dilute solutions is proportional to the mole concentration of the nonvolatile solute. Raoult then related the lowering of the vapor pressure of the solution to the lowering of the freezing point and the elevation of the boiling point. The change in boiling and freezing points is constant for a given solvent, and dependent only on the concentration of the solute, not the kind.

II. Illustration

This phenomenon serves as a basis for molecular weight determinations.

If both components of a solution are volatile, each will lower the vapor pressure of the other and the ratios of the two substances in the liquid and vapor phases will not necessarily be the same. Use is made of this fact to separate the two substances by distillation.

The addition of table salt (NaCl), which is nonvolatile, to distilled water would lower the vapor pressure in proportion to the amount of salt dissolved.

The resulting lower vapor pressure must reduce the rate of evaporation of the solution; this reasoning finally explains why old-timers put salt in their beer.

III. Magnitude

The effect is independent of temperature; the percent difference between vapor pressure of the solution and that of the pure solvent is the same for all temperatures. The change (°C) in boiling point (t_b) and freezing point (t_f) per mole of solute for 100 g of several solvents follows:

Solvent	t_b	t_f
Ethyl alcohol	1.20	—
Benzene	2.57	5.12
Water	0.511	1.860

IV. References

1. MacDougall, Frank H., *Physical Chemistry*, The Macmillan Co., New York, 1952, pp. 245–247. Raoult's law and limitations.
2. Eggert, John, *Physical Chemistry* (translated by S. J. Gregg), Constable and Co., Ltd., London, 1932, pp. 244–247. Babo and Raoult's Law relation.

See also Arrhenius Theory of Electrolytic Dissociation.

Quantities

Concentration	Liquid	Solid	Vapor pressure
Gas	Molecular weight	Temperature	

RESIDUAL VOLTAGE

I. Description

Some materials may retain a small amount of residual voltage when the applied potential has been removed.

II. Illustration

This effect has been reported for bismuth, antimony, and tellurium. Some semi-conductors in powdered form apparently exhibit this effect also. To date no application for this phenomenon is known.

III. Magnitude

About 1% of the applied voltage remains for one to three seconds. A magnetic field may influence this potential slightly.

IV. References

1. Brentano, J. C. M., and Colman Goldberg, "The Electrical Conductance of Pressed Powders, in Particular Zinc Oxide," *Physical Review* Vol. 94, No. 1, April 1, 1954, pp. 56–60. A discussion of this effect for semi-conductors powdered in air.
2. Geipel, H., "The Behavior of Bi, Sb, and Te with A.C. and D.C.," *Ann der Physik,* Vol. 38, May 7, 1912, pp. 149–205. An abstract appears in English in *Science Abstracts,* 1912, Vol. A, Abstract 1095.

Quantities

Charge	Current	Magnetic flux	Potential	Time

RESISTANCE/DIMENSION

I. Description

When a material undergoes a change in dimension, but is not strained, the change in resistance will be proportional to the length and inversely proportional to the cross-sectional area. If the material is strained, an additional factor will enter into the calculations.

II. Illustration

If fine wire is mounted to a paper backing, and then the entire unit attached to some material, the unit can be used as a very sensitive means of determining the strain in that material. Such a device finds wide use in aircraft structural work.

III. Magnitude

A strain measuring device as described in the illustration has a change in resistance of 2 to 3.5 times the change in length of the material. That is,

$$\frac{R_2/L_2}{R_1/L_1} = 2 \text{ to } 3.5$$

IV. Reference

1. Hetényi, M. I., *Handbook of Experimental Stress Analysis,* John Wiley and Sons, 1950, pp. 170–175. This section covers metallic resistance gages, mathematically and in practice. The general use of this type of gage is covered on pages 160–237. *See also* Skin Effect.

Quantities

Length   Resistivity   Strain

RESISTANCE—PRESSURE EFFECT

I. Description

Most materials change their resistance when subjected to a hydrostatic pressure. The magnitude and direction of resistance change vary widely with the material and probably the previous history of the sample.

II. Illustration

Cesium exhibits a wide change in resistance with pressure, but most materials exhibit at least a small change. Hysteresis and seasoning effects are often apparent.

III. Magnitude

Some resistance changes for some materials may be tabulated:

Material	Resistance Ratio	Pressure Range
Cesium	2:1	5–22 kg/cm²
N type germanium	1–4½	0–30,000 kg/cm²
P type germanium	1–0.94	0–30,000 kg/cm²

IV. Reference

1. Bridgman, P. W., "The Effect of Pressure on the Electrical Resistance of Certain Semi-Conductors" and "The Electrical Resistance to 30,000 kg/cm² of Twenty-Nine Metals and Intermetallic Compounds" *Proceedings of the American Academy of Arts and Sciences,* Vol. 79, No. 3, pp. 123–179, April, 1951. A description of resistance vs. pressure for many materials, also temperature coefficients for most of these.

Quantities

Chemical composition   Pressure   Resistivity

RESISTANCE/TEMPERATURE

I. Description

The resistance of all pure metals increases as the temperature of the metal is increased. The resistivity of nonmetals and electrolytes decreases as their temperature is increased.

II. Illustration

This effect is utilized in precision temperature detectors as well as in determining the average temperature of windings in electrical apparatus.

III. Magnitude

The variation of resistance with temperature for pure metals is linear enough to be represented by a temperature coefficient of resistivity. Heat treatment or mechanical strain may have a marked effect on the coefficient of a given metal.

$$\rho = \rho_0 + at$$

where ρ = resistivity
ρ_0 = resistivity at a base temperature
a = coefficient of resistance change
t = temperature elevation from base temperature

Temperature coefficients for alloys should be used within the range of ordinary temperatures. For instance, the coefficient for nichrome $(0.00017/°C)$ gives accurate results up to 450°C. But from 450 to 1000°C, there is no change in resistivity and the coefficient would give erroneous results. Manganin is an alloy for which the coefficient is essentially zero throughout the range of ambient temperatures. It is used in precision instruments, shunts, and laboratory standard resistors.

The formula for resistance does not hold for some materials such as mercury, tin, lead, zinc aluminum, cupric sulfide, tungsten carbide, and columbium nitride which become nearly perfect conductors near absolute zero ($15°K$ and below). Use of this effect is made in bolometers, high "Q" resonators, and low noise level photoconductors.

Nonmetals and solutions of acids and salts are not sufficiently linear to apply a temperature coefficient over any appreciable range. In general, their resistance varies with temperature as:

$$\rho = \rho_0 + at + bt^2 + ct^3 + \ldots$$

and the terms in t^2 and higher powers cannot be neglected.

Some temperature coefficients of resistivity taken at 20°C are:

	a
Aluminum	0.004
Copper	0.0039
Mercury	0.0008
Silver	0.004
Tungsten	0.005
Manganin	0.00002
Trophet A (80 Ni, 20 Cr)	0.05
Rubber (range: 10–30°C)	0.04
Varnished cambric (range: 10–30°C)	0.07

IV. References

1. Hehre, F. W., and G. T. Harness, *Electrical Circuits and Machinery,* John Wiley and Sons, New York, Vol. 1, 1942, pp. 97–102.
2. Little, Arthur D., "Low Temperatures in Electronics," *Electronics,* July, 1953, Vol. 26, No. 7, pp. 222–230. A qualitative review of current knowledge.
3. Astin, A. V. (Director), *Low Temperature Physics,* National Bureau of Standards, Circular 519, October 6, 1952, Washington, D. C. A total of 61 papers on various aspects of low temperature phenomena, a number of which deal with super conductivity.
4. Schoenberg, D., *Super Conductivity,* Cambridge University Press, London, 1952. Practical and theoretical aspects.

Quantities

Chemical composition   Resistivity   Temperature

RICHARDSON'S EFFECT (Edison Effect)

I. Description

There is a current of negative electricity, increasing rapidly with the temperature, flowing from all metallic conductors at a temperature of more than 1000°C to surrounding conductors, especially if the intervening space is completely vacuous. Knowledge of the existence of this current is chiefly due to Richardson. The study of this subject is given the name of thermionics.

II. Illustration

This current was first detected by Edison as a blue or purple glow inside an imperfectly exhausted carbon filament lamp. He studied the effect by adding another electrode (the plate) into the bulb, building a rectifier.

As first observed by Edison and for most vacuum tubes today, the current is a small fraction of an ampere, but modern thyratrons may carry 100 or more amperes.

III. Magnitude

The number of electrons emitted per unit time increases with the temperature of the filament and depends upon the substance of which it is made. The rate of electron emission is expressed as the current per unit of surface area of the hot body.

$$I = AT^2 e^{-b/T}$$

where I = amp/sq cm
T = temperatures in degrees K
A = constant for pure metal hot bodies is 60.2
b = constant, experimentally determined

Some representative values of the thermionic emission constants are:

	A	b	Melting Point, °K
Calcium	60.2	26,000	1,083
Carbon	60.2	46,500	3,773
Cesium	16.2	21,000	299
Molybdenum	60.2	51,500	2,893
Nickel	26.8	32,100	1,725
Platinum	60.2	59,000	2,028
Tantalum	60.2	47,200	3,123
Thorium	60.2	38,900	2,118
Tungsten	60.2	52,400	3,643

IV. References

1. Richtmyer, F. K., and E. H. Kennard, *Introduction to Modern Physics,* McGraw-Hill Book Co., New York, 1955. Various aspects of thermionic emission.
2. Wright, D. A., "A Survey of Present Knowledge of Thermionic Emitters," *The Proceedings of the Institute of Electrical Engineers,* Vol. 100, No. 65, Part III, May, 1953, London, pp. 125–142. A review of present knowledge.
3. Zemansky, Mark W., *Heat and Thermodynamics,* McGraw-Hill Book Co., New York, 1955. Application of sublimation equation to electron gas.

Quantities

Chemical composition   Current   Emissivity   Temperature

SCHRODINGER'S WAVE EQUATION

I. Description

This equation relates the properties of matter which at times suggest that matter is corpuscular, and at other times suggest that matter is an electromagnetic wave.

II. Illustration

The equation is similar to those obtained for heat flow in a body. No solutions to the wave equation can have a simple sine or cosine function.

III. Magnitude

The equation is:

$$\frac{-\hbar}{2\pi i} \frac{\partial \psi}{\partial t} = \frac{-\hbar^2}{8\pi^2 m} \left(\frac{\partial^2 \psi}{\partial x^2} + \frac{\partial^2 \psi}{\partial y^2} + \frac{\partial^2 \psi}{\partial z^2} \right) + V\psi$$

where
ψ = equation of the wave
V = potential energy function of particle
$\hbar$ = Planck's constant = 6.610×10^{-27} erg sec
t = time
x, y, z = three coordinate directions
$i = \sqrt{-1}$
m = mass of the particle

Reference should be made to the simpler De Broglie equations to determine the wavelength of the particles,

$$\lambda = \frac{\hbar}{mv}$$

where λ = the wavelength
m = mass of particle
v = velocity

These equations are important only when dealing with small particles at high velocities; example, electrons in tubes.

IV. Reference

1. Richtmyer, F. K., E. H. Kennard, and T. Lauritsen, *Introduction to Modern Physics*, McGraw-Hill Book Co., New York, 1955. Derivation and physical significance.

Quantities

Energy (P.E.)	Mass	Time
Frequency	Propagation	Velocity

SHOT EFFECT (SCHOTTKY EFFECT)

I. Description

Shot noise is generated in electron tubes because electrons emitted from the cathode are random in time and velocity. Thus, the plate current is not exactly uniform, the shot noise components being distributed uniformly in frequency as is thermal agitation noise. The voltage variation developed is termed the shot effect.

II. Illustration

This shot noise or shot effect is an important factor in limiting the maximum permissible gain from vacuum tube amplifiers since it may well mask the signal.

III. Magnitude

For temperature limited emission in a diode, the voltage variations are:

$$\overline{E^2} = 3.18 \times 10^{-19} IZ^2 \, df$$

where $\overline{E^2}$ = mean square shot effect voltage
  I = electron current, amp
  Z = resonant impedance of the tuned circuit
  df = frequency bandwidth factor

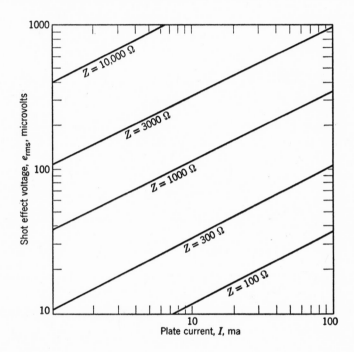

IV. References

1. M.I.T. Radar School Staff, *Principles of Radar,* McGraw-Hill Book Co., New York, 1952, pp. 358.
2. Lawson, James L., and George E. Uhlenbeck, *Threshold Signals,* McGraw-Hill Book Co., New York, 1950, pp. 64–97. Thermal and shot noises.

Quantities

Current   Emissivity   Potential   Sound   Temperature

SKIN EFFECT

I. Description

When a wire is carrying an alternating current, or, in general, any current whose magnitude is varying, the current has a tendency to crowd toward the surface of the wire. The result will be a reduction of the inductance and an increase in the ohmic resistance of the conductor.

II. Illustration

The existence of this effect may be seen from the following analysis. Assume the wire to be divided into a large number of very small circular elements all exactly alike and parallel to the conductor axis. Assume also that the wire is carrying a current which is uniformly distributed throughout the cross section and that this current begins to increase in value. The elements near the axis have more flux encircling them and hence have a higher self-inductance (because of the higher number of flux linkages) than those near the surface. Hence, an easier path for current will lie toward the surface of the conductor, and since the material is uniform, the current will seek to flow in this easier path. This effect does not hold true at temperatures near absolute zero.

This skin effect is utilized in the construction of wave guides (silver-plated) and coaxial cable.

III. Magnitude

The correction factor, σ, to be applied to the inductance and resistance of a solid round wire is given from the following graph and formulas:

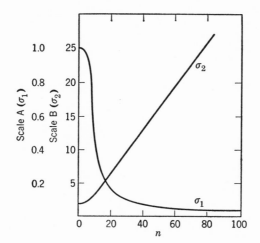

$$n = a\sqrt{\frac{8\pi^2 f\mu}{\rho}} \qquad n = 0.214a\sqrt{f} \text{ (for copper)}$$

where a = wire radius in cm

f = frequency in cps

ρ = resistivity in abohms/cm^3

μ = permeability

Inductance for parallel wires:

$$L = \sigma_1(1.482) \log \frac{d - r}{r} \text{ mh/mile}$$

where d = distance between wires

r = radius of wire

Resistance for a conductor (taking into account skin effect, a correction must be applied to d-c ohmic resistance):

$$R_{\text{eff}} = \sigma_2 R_{\text{d-c}}$$

IV. References

1. Ware, L. A., and H. R. Reed, *Communication Circuits*, John Wiley and Sons, New York, 3rd Ed., 1949.

2. P. M. Marcus, *Low Temperature Physics*, National Bureau of Standards, Circular 519, Washington, D. C., 1951, pp. 265–272. "Approximate Calculations of the Surface Impedance of a Metal in the Anomalous Region." Theory, and results for low temperatures.
See also Proximity Effect.

Quantities

Current	Inductance	Permeability	Temperature
Frequency	Length	Resistivity	

SNELL'S LAW

(The law of refraction)

I. Description

A. When light passes from one medium to another, the incident ray, the normal of the surface at the point of incidence, the reflected ray, and the refracted ray are all in the same plane.

B. The sine of the angle of incidence bears to the sine of the angle of refraction a ratio which is constant for the same two media and depends only on the nature of these media. If the light is traveling from a material of a high to a material with a low index of refraction, the light is totally reflected if the angle exceeds a limiting critical angle.

C. Dispersion is the spreading of component wavelengths in a beam of radiation caused by a variation of the index of refraction with wavelength.

II. Illustration

All lenses (not reflectors) depend upon refraction to obtain their action. Dispersion which causes chromatic aberration in lenses is utilized in prisms to form spectra. Bundles of light transmitting fibers have been used to transmit image details to a remote position. Refraction is also used in microwave lenses.

III. Magnitude

The angles of incidence, indices of refraction, and propagation velocities are related by the equation:

$$\frac{v_i}{v_r} = \frac{\sin \theta_i}{\sin \theta_r} = \frac{\eta_r}{\eta_i}$$

where v = velocity of radiation
i = (subscript) incident ray
r = (subscript) refracted ray
θ = angle (measured from normal)
η = index of refraction of medium

Total reflection occurs if the critical angle θ_i is reached:

$$\sin \theta_i = \frac{\eta_i}{\eta_r}$$

Since $\eta_i = 1$ for air, this may readily be used to determine the index of refraction for a material. For some materials this angle of total reflection (with air) is:

	θ_i
Water	48°27′40″
Crown glass	40°30′
Lead chromate	19°28′20″
Quartz	40°22′
Diamond	24°26′

The specific refraction r, or refractivity, is:

$$r = \frac{1}{d}\left(\frac{n^2 - 1}{n^2 + 2}\right)$$

where n = refractive index
d = density of the liquid
Both at the same temperature

Molar refraction, **R**, is:

$$\mathbf{R} = \left(\frac{M}{d}\right)\left(\frac{n^2 - 1}{n^2 + 2}\right)$$

where M = molecular weight

Since molar refraction theoretically stays constant at all temperatures, this equation gives the approximate measure of volume occupied by molecules in a molar volume of a substance.

IV. References

1. Page, Leigh, *Theoretical Physics,* D. Van Nostrand Co., New York, 1952, pp. 582–587. Mathematical treatments of refraction at plane and spherical surfaces; pp. 588–592, lenses.
2. Hausmann, E., and E. Slack, *Physics,* D. Van Nostrand Co., New York, 1948, pp. 643–645. An understandable discussion (with mathematics), including the effect of flat plates.
3. MacDougall, Frank H., *Physical Chemistry,* The Macmillan Co., New York, 1952, pp. 200–201. Description and one example of specific and molar refraction.
See also Diffraction, Gladstone and Dale's Law.

Quantities

Angle	Frequency	Light	Molecular	Speed of
Density	Index of	Magnification	weight	light
	refraction			Temperature

STARK EFFECT

I. Description

The spectral lines emitted when the source is in a strong electric field are split and polarized. The effects vary with field intensity and with the direction between the direction of emission and the electric field.

In many respects this resembles the more complicated types of Zeeman effect, but is subject to different laws, and the lines change in character radically and in multiplicity of component lines with increasing field intensity.

II. Illustration

When the hydrogen lines $H\alpha$ and $H\beta$ are under observation in a direction perpendicular to the electric field, three evenly spaced lines appear which are unpolarized.

III. Magnitude

The hydrogen violet line separates as much as 33 A apart for a field 74,000 volts/cm. This splitting of the spectral lines is linear with the square of the applied field strength.

IV. References

1. Richtmyer, F. K., E. H. Kennard, and T. Lauritsen, *Introduction to Modern Physics,* McGraw-Hill Book Co., New York, 1955. Description of apparatus.
2. White, Harvey Elliott, *Introduction to Atomic Spectra,* McGraw-Hill Book Co., New York, 1934, pp. 401–407. Theory, some mathematics, and some examples.

Quantities

| Electric flux | Emissivity | Frequency | Light |

STATE AND CHANGE OF STATE

I. Description

Matter may exist in three forms or phases: solid, liquid, and gas. The highest temperature and pressure at which all three of these states may coexist in equilibrium is called the triple point. The highest temperature at which a gas may be converted to a liquid by an increase in pressure is termed the critical point, and the variables are termed the critical temperature and the critical pressure of the gas. Sublimation is the changing of a solid directly to a gas.

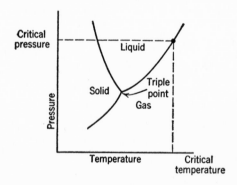

Unstable situations such as supercooling and superheating arise when dealing with pure liquids. Supercooling is the cooling of a liquid to a temperature below its normal freezing point with no accompanying change in state. Superheating occurs when the boiling temperature is reached, but the liquid is not agitated by the liberation of vapor in its bulk. When either of these situations arise, when the change does start, it is very rapid and violent.

II. Illustration

Regelation (snowballs), or the melting of ice under pressure, is a common example of this relationship of state to pressure and temperature. Boilers have been constructed which heat the water under a pressure greater than critical so that the steam is formed only at the turbine nozzle. Similar expansions are used to make liquid gases for industrial and scientific use. (See also Le Châtelier's Law.)

III. Magnitude

The melting point of ice is lowered 0.0130°F per atmosphere of pressure up to 700 atmospheres. At a pressure below 4.6 mm of mercury, ice when heated is converted into water vapor without melting.

IV. References

1. Hodgman, Charles D., *Handbook of Chemistry and Physics,* Chemical Rubber Publishing Co., Cleveland, 37th Ed., 1955. Critical constants of gases.
2. Hausmann, E., and E. Slack, *Physics,* D. Van Nostrand Co., New York, 1948, pp. 262–268. Discussion of this change of state.
3. MacDougall, Frank H., *Physical Chemistry,* The Macmillan Co., New York, 1952, pp. 367–376. Water; p. 230, Clapeyron equation describes the coexistence of two phases in equilibrium of a substance at one temperature and corresponding pressure.

Quantities

Boiling point	Enthalpy	Gas	Pressure	Temperature
Chemical composition	Freezing point	Liquid	Solid	

STEFAN-BOLTZMANN LAW (Kirchhoff's Law)
(Black body radiation)

I. Description

The Stefan-Boltzmann law states that the total radiation from black body is proportional to the fourth power of its absolute temperature. A black body is defined as a body that absorbs all the radiant energy falling upon it.

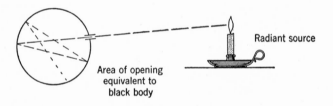

Kirchhoff devised a scheme for making a practical and near perfect black body. Kirchhoff also found that the relation between the powers of emission and the powers of absorption for rays of the same wavelength is constant for all bodies at the same temperature.

1. A substance when excited by some means or other possesses a certain power of emission to emit definite rays, whose wavelengths depend upon the nature of the substance and upon its temperature.

2. The substance exerts a definite absorptive power, which is a maximum for the rays it tends to emit.

3. At a given temperature, the ratio between the emissive and the absorptive power for a given wavelength is the same for all bodies and is equal to the emissive power of a perfectly black body.

II. Illustration

The effect of the law is used to determine temperature.

A furnace with a small opening in it is similar to Kirchhoff's sphere.

The area of the small opening is effectively the black body. All the heat which passes through this area is absorbed. If an optical means were used to concentrate this radiant energy on a thermocouple junction, a millivoltmeter could be calibrated to give the temperature of that part of the furnace which the small opening sees.

III. Magnitude

The Stefan-Boltzmann law may be stated in mathematical form:

$$q_b = 0.174 \times 10^{-8} A(T)^4$$

where q_b = total heat radiated from a black body, Btu/hr

A = area of radiating surface (sq ft)

T = absolute temperature of the black body, degree Rankine

Since black body conditions are not always present, the equation for total radiation may be modified with an emissivity factor for the particular material, surface condition, and temperature.

IV. References

1. Richtmyer, F. K., E. H. Kennard, and T. Lauritsen, *Introduction to Modern Physics,* McGraw-Hill Book Co., New York, 5th Ed., 1955. Pp. 110–113, the derivation of the Stefan-Boltzmann law; pp. 114–132, general discussion on radiation.
2. Koller, Lewis R., *Ultraviolet Radiation,* John Wiley and Sons, New York, 1952, pp. 90–105. Stefan-Boltzmann law and its relation to various light sources.
3. Zemansky, Mark W., *Heat and Thermodynamics,* McGraw-Hill Book Co., New York, 1951, pp. 86–88. Description of Kirchhoff's law and emissivity tables.

Quantities

Absorption	Frequency	Radiation
Emissivity	Light	Temperature

STOKES'S LAW

I. Description

Stokes's law is a derived expression for the force necessary to keep a small sphere moving at a uniform speed through a fluid.

II. Illustration

This law is very useful in the study of drops or other spherical particles falling in free air. Variations are used in aerodynamics.

This law was used by Millikan to measure ionic charges; hence the charge on an electron.

III. Magnitude

The basic equation (involving the force of gravity) is:

$$V_s = \frac{2gr^2}{9N} (\sigma - \rho)$$

where N = viscosity of medium, poises
r = radius of particle
σ = density of drop
ρ = density of medium
V_s = velocity of fall of spherical particle under gravity
g = force of gravity

In order for the equation to hold, the following assumptions must be satisfied:

1. That the inhomogeneities in the medium are small in comparison with the size of the sphere.
2. That the sphere falls as it would in a medium of unlimited extent.
3. That the sphere is smooth and rigid.

4. That there is no slipping of the medium over the surface of the sphere.

5. That the velocity with which the sphere is moving is so small that the resistance to motion is all due to the viscosity of the medium and not to its inertia.

A practical form of the above equation is:

$$V_s = K''SD^2N^{-1} = K_3SD^2$$

where N = viscosity of gas, poises
V = velocity, fpm
D = diameter of particle, microns (0.001 mm)
S = specific gravity of particle
K_3 = 0.0059 for spheres falling in normal air (1 atm),
0.0039 for irregular shapes.

This equation holds for streamline flow for diameters of 2 to 50 microns.

If a steel ball is falling free in a tank of 80°F water, what will the terminal velocity be?

$$V = \frac{2gr^2}{9N}(\sigma - \rho) = 4.31 \text{ cm/sec}$$

where g = 97.8 cm/sec^2
r = 0.5 cm
σ = 7.85 dyne-sec^2/cm^4
ρ = 1.0 dyne-sec^2/cm^4
N = 86.1 dyne-sec/cm^2

Viscosity of air at one atmosphere at 23°C is approximately 0.0001823 poise. For gases it increases with temperature; for liquids it decreases.

Typical size ranges of particles to which this equation is often applied are:

Fog	1 to 40 microns
Pigments	1 to 7 microns
Fly ash	3 to 70 microns
Bacteria	1 to 15 microns
Pollens	20 to 69 microns

IV. Reference

1. Page, Leigh, *Introduction to Theoretical Physics,* D. Van Nostrand Co., New York, 3rd Ed., 1952. Mathematical derivation.

Quantities

| Density | Length | Velocity |
| Gas | Temperature | Viscosity |

STOKES'S LAW OF FLUORESCENCE

I. Description

If a material is illuminated by radiation which it is capable of absorbing, the material may emit light. According to Stokes's law, the wavelength of the fluorescent, or emitted light, is always longer than the absorbed light. Since the atoms may already have energy, Stokes's law does not strictly apply, but is applicable if the "center of gravity" of the fluorescent light is considered.

When light is emitted after the excitation is removed, the phenomenon is termed phosphorescence, even though the mechanism for light production is the same.

The Raman effect, which is related to the Stokes's law, has been observed when the incident radiations upon the material do not have a wavelength corresponding to one of the absorption bands or lines of the material. This effect is much less intense than most fluorescent light, and is observed as lines toward the red of the exciting line and still fainter lines on the violet side. (This latter case is sometimes observed in fluorescence and is a violation of Stokes's law. These lines are called anti-Stokes's lines.)

II. Illustration

Fluorescent lamps which utilize the ultraviolet light produced by a low-pressure mercury discharge and then convert this energy to visible light are perhaps the most common example of fluorescence which illustrate the shift in wavelength.

Fluorescent effects are usually demonstrated by light from a mercury arc filtered by a nickel oxide glass to remove visible light.

III. Magnitude

The ratio of light emitted to light absorbed is termed the fluorescence efficiency. Producing 30 lumens per watt, fluorescent lamps have about three times the efficiency of incandescent ones.

Some common fluorescent materials illustrate the frequency shift. All materials were illuminated by 3650 A ultraviolet light.

Material	Fluorescence (not line emission)
Ethyl acetate	Blue (4900 A)
Fluorescin	Blue green (5000 A)
Glycerin	Purplish blue (4200 A)

Some laundry bleaches also fluoresce.

IV. References

1. Preston, Thomas, *The Theory of Light,* Macmillan and Co., Ltd., London, 1929, pp. 518–521. Some fluorescing materials.
2. De Ment, Jack, *Fluorescent Chemicals,* Chemical Publishing Co., Brooklyn, New York, 1942. The book is useful as a summary of experimental fact.
3. Jenkins and White, *Fundamentals of Optics,* McGraw-Hill Book Co., New York, 1950. Short description of the Raman effect, p. 456.

See also Luminescence.

Quantities

Absorption	Color	Energy (K.E.)	Intensity
Chemical composition	Emissivity	Frequency	Light

STRESS-STRAIN EFFECTS

I. Description

Hooke's law

As long as the strain is kept below a certain limit for each material, called the elastic limit, the stress is proportional to the strain.

$$K = F/x$$

where K = Young's modulus
F = force per unit area (stress)
x = deformation per unit length (strain)

Elastic limit

The elastic limit is the maximum stress to which a body may be subjected without causing permanent deformation.

Poisson's ratio

The longitudinal stretching of any elastic material is accompanied by a lateral contraction. The ratio of the lateral contraction to the elongation per unit length is known as Poisson's ratio:

$$M = \frac{\text{percent lateral contraction}}{\text{percent elongation under stress}}$$

Creep

Constant loads maintained over a long period of time may result in a gradual deformation known as creep. The combination of high stress and high temperature may eventually result in rupture of the material.

Elastic fatigue

Repeated loads may result in a progressive failure known as fatigue. The limiting stress below which a material will withstand stress cycles indefinitely is called the endurance limit.

Work hardening

As a material is permanently deformed by stresses exceeding the elastic limit, it becomes stronger and greater stresses are necessary to cause further deformation.

Photoelasticity

Certain materials become doubly refracting when subjected to a mechanical stress. Polarized light passing through doubly refracting areas caused by stress will be rotated through an angle proportional to the stress.

Stress corrosion

All kinds of corrosion are accelerated by the presence of stresses.

II. Illustration

Hooke's law is commonly recognized in the deflection characteristics of springs and beams. A few materials such as concrete, copper, and cast iron have proportional limits below their elastic limit.

Poisson's ratio must be applied to account for changes in resistance and density as well as changes in dimension when a material is stretched or compressed.

Creep is a significant problem in the design of high temperature, high stress structures such as boilers and turbines. Elastic fatigue may be encountered whenever the load is varying.

Work hardening is involved in many metal-working processes, such as cold rolling, bending, upsetting, swaging, and coining.

Photoelasticity has become an important tool in the field of stress analysis. Transparent bakelite models are made of complicated parts, stressed and observed in polarized light through an analyzing lens. Lines of constant stress appear as light and dark contours over the face of the model. Isoclinic lines may also be plotted by this method.

III. Magnitude

Creep is observed in materials such as lead and asphalt at room temperature. The effect becomes significant for steel at temperatures exceeding 700°F. Stainless steel (18-8) creeps 1% in 100,000 hours (11.4 years) when a stress of 12,000 psi is maintained at a 1000°F temperature.

TENSION PROPERTIES OF SOME MATERIALS

	Elastic Limit, psi	Young's Modulus, psi	Poisson's Ratio
Aluminum (pure, annealed)	2,000	9,500,000	0.36
Duralumin (hardened)	30,000	10,500,000	0.33
High brass (annealed)	20,000	15,000,000	0.33
High brass (cold-worked)	30,000	14,000,000	0.33
Cast iron (93 Fe, 4 C, 2 Si)	20,000	14,000,000	0.21
Cast iron (93.5 Fe, 3.5 C, 2 Si)	50,000	23,000,000	0.30
Steel (structural, hot-rolled)	30,000	28,000,000	0.26
Steel (spring, heat-treated)	150,000	28,500,000	—
Rubber (pure gum)	1,500	300	—
Rubber (vulcanized hard)	10,000	300,000	—

IV. Reference

1. Young, J. F., *Materials and Processes,* Wiley and Sons, New York, 1954.

Quantities

Chemical composition	Length	Strain	Time
Force	Light	Stress	Volume
Frequency	Polarization	Temperature	Yield point

SURFACE TENSION

I. Description

Cohesion in fluids as evidenced by surface tension is the mutual molecular attraction in the fluid, and is manifest primarily as a surface force where two fluids or a fluid and gas come together.

II. Illustration

The spherical shape of fluid drops is due to this cause as well as the spherical shape of bubbles. (Neither is exactly spherical under usual conditions.) In capillary attraction the wetting of the glass by water draws the water up until the upward pull of the surface tension is equalized by the weight of the fluid column. Utilization of nonwetting coatings allows effective raincoats to be made of permeable materials.

III. Magnitude

Surface tension may be expressed as dynes per centimeter or as ergs per square centimeter.

The total force along both sides of a line on the surface of a fluid is given by:

$$F = LT$$

where L = length of the line
T = surface tension of liquid

Capillary tubes may be used to determine the surface tension of a liquid:

$$T = \frac{rhdg}{2}$$

where T = surface tension, dynes/cm
r = internal tube radius in cm
h = height of liquid column in cm
d = density of the fluid, grams/cm^3
g = gravity acceleration, cm/sec^2

This expression may be inverted to determine the rise of liquids in a capillary. This expression is similar to Jurin's law.

The pressure in a drop due to surface tension is:

$$p = \frac{2T}{r}$$

where p = pressure in dynes/cm^2

Or for a bubble in a fluid it is:

$$p = \frac{4T}{r}$$

Where the fluid is a solution, surface tension is also related to the concentration of the solute. Inorganic salts in water increase the surface tension slightly, while organic salts decrease the surface tension. The effect is temperature sensitive as may be seen by the table of water against air.

Temperature, °C	T, dynes/cm
0	75.6
10	74.2
30	71.2
100	58.9

For some other materials:

Materials	Temperature, °C	T, dynes/cm
Benzene against mercury	20	357
Water against ethyl ether	20	10.7
Water against benzene	20	379
Mercury against air	15	787

The surface tension between two saturated solutions is given by Antonoff's rule which states that the surface tension of one liquid to the other is the surface tension of the first to the same gas minus that of the second to the same gas.

IV. References

1. Hodgman, C. D., *Handbook of Chemistry and Physics,* Chemical Rubber Publishing Co., Cleveland, Ed. 37, 1955. Tables of values.
2. MacDougall, Frank H., *Physical Chemistry,* The Macmillan Co., New York, 3rd Ed., 1952, pp. 90–97 and 710. Meniscus, capillary rise, bubbles, effect of temperature.

Quantities

Concentration	Length	Pressure	Temperature
Force	Liquid	Surface tension	

THERMODYNAMICS LAWS

I. Description

First Law. Energy can be neither created nor destroyed. When mechanical work is transformed into heat or heat into work, the amount of work is always equivalent to the quantity of heat.

Second Law. Heat cannot flow spontaneously from lower to higher temperatures. It is impossible for any inanimate machine to derive mechanical energy from any portion of matter by cooling it below the temperature of the coldest of the surrounding objects.

Third Law. It is impossible by any finite number of operations, even if idealized, to reduce any system to the absolute zero of temperature.

II. Illustration

It may be argued that these laws are statistical and do not apply to molecules individually. For example, the conservation of energy does not seem to hold for certain nuclear reactions where beta particles are emitted. The existence of a so-called neutrino particle must be assumed in order to preserve the validity of the law.

Maxwell pointed out that the second law would not hold if individual molecules could be separated according to their velocities. Maxwell imagined a superhuman creature who could do this, but so far no mechanical substitute has been found for Maxwell's demon.

The second law has also been expressed as the principle of increase of entropy. Entropy is a measure of the disorder of molecular movements in a system. When a wheel is braked to a stop, the orderly rotation of molecules becomes a random vibration known as heat and the entropy is increased. It is highly improbable that these mixed-up motions will reorganize themselves and start the wheel rolling again.

III. Magnitude

A thermodynamic cycle is a repeating series of processes performed upon a medium in order to convert heat into mechanical energy. The most efficient cycle possible is the theoretical Carnot cycle where:

$$\text{efficiency} = \frac{Q_1 - Q_2}{Q_1} = \frac{T_1 - T_2}{T_1}$$

where Q_1 = heat input
   Q_2 = heat rejected
   T_1 = absolute temperature of hot source
   T_2 = absolute temperature of cold source

A Carnot engine would be prohibitively large and slow-moving; in practice, several other cycles are used:

CYCLE DIAGRAMS

$P - V$ $T - S$

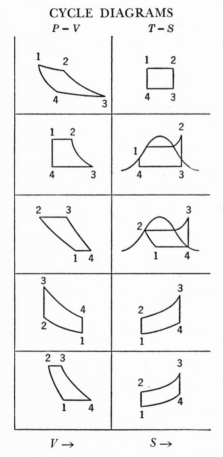

$V \rightarrow$ $S \rightarrow$

Carnot cycle. Isothermal expansion, adiabatic expansion, isothermal compression, adiabatic compression.

Rankine cycle (steam engine). Constant pressure heating, adiabatic expansion, constant pressure cooling, adiabatic compression.

Vapor refrigeration cycle (refrigerator). Adiabatic compression, constant pressure cooling, constant enthalpy expansion, constant pressure heating.

Otto cycle (internal combustion engine). Adiabatic compression, constant volume combustion, adiabatic expansion, constant volume heat rejection.

Brayton cycle (gas turbine). Adiabatic compression, constant pressure combustion, adiabatic expansion, constant pressure cooling.

IV. Reference

1. Lichty, L. C., *Thermodynamics*, McGraw-Hill Book Co., New York, 1948, Chapter 8. Discussion and analysis of cycles.

Quantities

Energy (K.E.)	Enthalpy	Heat flux	Pressure
Energy (P.E.)	Entropy	Power	Temperature

THERMOELASTIC EFFECT

I. Description

The thermoelastic effect (similar to the Thomson effect) is the production of an electrical potential between two points in a stressed metal when a constant temperature difference is maintained between the two points. The voltage produced varies both with the temperature difference and the stress intensity.

II. Illustration

Because thermoelectric currents are also generated, the method shown in the figure may be used only for varying stresses.

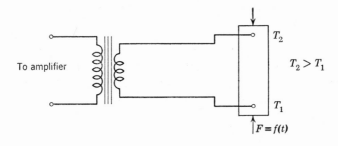

To amplifier

T_2

$T_2 > T_1$

T_1

$F = f(t)$

III. Magnitude

The voltage developed is of the same order of magnitude as the Thomson effect. The method has not, as yet, been used for applications requiring either high accuracy or sensitivity.

IV. References

1. Roberts, H. C., *Mechanical Measurements by Electrical Means,* The Instruments Publishing Co., Pittsburgh, Pennsylvania, 2nd Ed., 1951. Short discussion.

Quantities

Force   Potential   Strain   Stress   Temperature

THERMOELECTRIC EFFECTS

SEEBECK EFFECT

I. Description

When a circuit consists of two different metals, and the two junctions of these metals are at different temperatures, there will be a flow of electric current in the circuit. This current is a function of the type of metals and is nearly proportional to the temperature differences between junctions and inversely proportional to the circuit resistance.

The Seebeck effect may be thought of as the result of two opposing effects: the Thomson emf due to the temperature gradient across the length of each conductor and the Peltier emf due to the difference in temperature of the two junctions.

II. Illustration

Thermocouples use this principle for measuring a very wide range of temperatures.

III. Magnitude

A Chromel-Alumel thermocouple develops approximately 20 μv per °C difference in junction temperatures.

In the general case, when two metals are selected at random, the variation of emf with temperature is far from linear. The result is due to the combined effects described above.

If one junction of an iron-copper thermocouple is held at 0°C, the variation of emf developed by the thermocouple versus the temperature of the second junction is as follows:

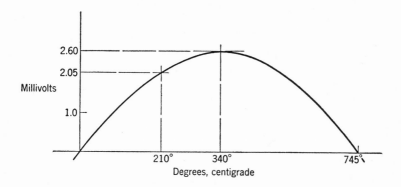

This means that current would flow across the hot junction from iron to copper at any temperature between 0 and 745°C. Current would flow in the opposite direction at temperatures above or below this.

PELTIER EFFECT

I. Description

This is the inverse of the Seebeck effect. When a current flows across the junction of two unlike metals, it gives rise to an absorption or liberation of heat. If the current flows in the same direction as the current at the hot junction of a thermoelectric circuit of the two metals, heat is absorbed; if it flows in the same direction as the current at the cold junction of the thermoelectric circuit, heat is liberated.

The heat developed in a junction of two metals is proportional to the first power of the current, and depends on the direction of the current.

The quantity of heat absorbed or liberated is given by the following equations:

$$\text{Rate heat is absorbed} = IT\,(dE/dt)$$

where I = current in amp

          T = absolute temperature (°K)

     dE/dt = rate of change of thermo emf with temperature

II. Illustration

The Peltier effect is an aspect of the thermoelectric effect and the magnitude is directly proportional to the thermoelectric power of the combination of the metals used, as well as the current through the junction.

The fundamental requirements for a Peltier couple are:

1. High contrasting thermoelectric power
2. Low heat conductivity
3. High electric conductivity

The useful Peltier cooling effect is less than total heat abstraction because of:

1. I^2R loss in the junction
2. I^2R loss in the materials
3. Heat from the surrounding medium
4. Conduction of heat from the hot junction

It is noted that two of the four factors depend upon the square of the current while the Peltier cooling is proportional to the first power of the current; therefore, for a given couple there is an optimum current for the maximum attainable cooling.

The cold junction cannot be made cooler by making the hot junction cooler; in fact, the cold junction will get warmer because of the Thomson effect.

The Peltier couple is used as a calibrated refrigerator in a radiation detector where current required to hold temperature constant is a measure of heat input.

III. Magnitude

A. At a junction of Fe–Ni at 0°C, there would be liberated or absorbed 9.4×10^{-3} joule/second for each ampere of current. (This does not take into consideration any I^2R loss which would always liberate heat.) The efficiency of all thermoelectric couples is low, being not over 1 to 2% for most materials.

B. In actual tests, the Peltier effect efficiency has been found to be less than 1%. The best that can be done by use of ordinary metals is to cool a small bit of metal by not more than 10°C. These figures have been improved upon by the use of semi-conducting materials so that temperature differences of 20°C have been obtained. These semi-conducting materials have been used to build experimental refrigerators.

See also "Combined Equations," pages 218–219.

THOMSON AND BENEDICK EFFECTS

I. Description

Both these laws deal with the appearance and disappearance of heat in a heated conductor.

Thomson effect

In unequally heated conductors (such as copper), heat is liberated at points where the current and heat flow in the same direction and are absorbed when they flow in opposite directions. For copper, this tends to diminish the inequality of temperature, while for iron it tends to increase the difference.

Benedick effect (*see* Reference 6)

This is the converse of the Thomson effect. In a homogeneous conductor, a difference in potential between two points will produce a difference of temperature between these points.

For this effect, the difference in temperature between the ends of the rod is:

$$\Delta T = \frac{1}{\sigma} \int_{E_1}^{E_2} dE$$

where the limits of the integral are the voltages at either end of the rod and σ is the Thomson coefficient. In copper, the currents produced will tend to flow from the hot to the cold portions, while the action is reversed in iron. This effect is so very small that it is difficult to detect.

II. Illustration

These effects could be used to generate a small but accurate temperature difference.

If a thin sheet of copper is suspended vertically between the poles of a horseshoe magnet and one corner of the sheet is heated, the copper will tend to rotate because of the interaction of the circulating currents and the magnetic field. Lead has no measurable Thomson effect.

III. Magnitude

The currents produced are small; consequently, the temperature gradients must be sharp. The Thomson coefficient or specific heat of electricity is 1.0000 joule per coulomb per degree Centigrade.

COMBINED EQUATIONS

For the Seebeck or thermoelectric voltage of a couple:

$$E_{AB} = \int_{T_0}^{T} (S_A - S_B)\, dT$$

where E_{AB} = Seebeck emf in volts
T_0 = temperature of cold end of couple wires
T = temperature at junction
S_A = entropy transport factor material A
S_B = entropy transport factor material B

Thus the derivative shows difference of entropy transport factors:

$$\frac{dE_{AB}}{dT} = S_A - S_B$$

where $S_A - S_B$ is also known as the thermoelectric power of the couple.

For the Peltier effect, the rate of heat liberation at the junction will be:

$$W = I^2 R_J + I T_0 (S_A - S_B)$$

where W = watts at junction

   I = junction current flow from A to B

   T_0 = temperature at cold end

   R_J = junction resistance

The Peltier emf is $V_{AB} = T$ $(S_A - S_B)$.

The Thomson effect changes the heat liberation rate in a material as follows:

$$W = I^2 R + I \left(T_0 \frac{dS}{dT} \Delta T \right)$$

where R = resistance of length

   ΔT = temperature rise at one end of the length

The Thomson coefficient is:

$$\sigma = - T \frac{dS}{dT}$$

The Kelvin relations may be obtained by combining equations; the Peltier emf equals the temperature times the thermoelectric power of a couple:

$$V_{AB} = T \frac{(dE_{AB})}{(dT)}$$

and the difference of two Thomson coefficients is the negative of the temperature times the second derivative of the thermoelectric power with temperature:

$$\sigma_A - \sigma_B = - T \frac{d^2 E_{AB}}{dT^2}$$

If work is done in a thermoelectric circuit, the heat normally liberated at the cold junction and along the wires is decreased by the amount of work done.

IV. References

1. White, W. C., "Some Experiments with Peltier Effect," *Electrical Engineering*, July, 1951.
2. Wall, T. F., "The Peltier Effect," *The Electrician*, March 26, 1928.
3. Sears, F. W., *Principles of Physics*, Addison-Wesley Press, Cambridge, Mass., 1951, Vol. 2, pp. 160–168. Includes thermoelectric coefficients of metals and formulas for various emf's, the peak emf temperature, and the zero emf temperature.

4. Zemansky, Mark W., *Heat and Thermodynamics,* McGraw-Hill Book Co., New York, 3rd Ed., 1951. Description of these effects and thermodynamic aspects.
5. Harnwell, Gaylord P., *Principles of Electricity and Electro-Magnetism,* McGraw-Hill Book Co., New York, 1949, pp. 203–205. A somewhat theoretical discussion of Thomson effect.
6. Bridgman, P. W., *The Thermodynamics of Electrical Phenomena in Metals,* The Macmillan Co., New York, 1934, p. 40. This reference negates the Benedick effect.
7. Lee, J. F., and F. W. Sears, *Thermodynamics,* Addison-Wesley Publishing Co., Cambridge, Mass., pp. 178–185. Excellent theoretical formulas and relations of all these effects.

Quantities

Chemical	Current	Force	Potential
composition	Direction	Heat flux	Temperature
Conductivity			

TOTAL REFLECTION

I. Description

When light travels so as to pass from one medium to another in which its velocity is greater, refraction ceases and total reflection begins at a certain critical angle of incidence, θ, such that

$$\sin \theta = 1/n$$

where n is the index of the first medium with respect to the second. If the second medium is air, n has the usual value for the first medium.

For any other second medium,

$$n = \frac{n_1}{n_2} = \frac{q_2}{q_1}$$

where n_1 and n_2 are the indices of refraction for the first and second medium respectively, and q_1 and q_2 are the velocities of propagation in the first and second medium respectively.

II. Illustration

Perfectly reflecting mirrors may be made by this principle. Prisms used in binoculars use this technique. Bundles of light-transmitting fibres have been used to transmit image details to a remote position. One could expect to apply this behavior to all wavelike phenomena that radiate in wave fronts.

III. Magnitude

The angle for total reflection for light in some materials is:

Water	48°27'40"
Crown glass	40°30'
Lead chromate	19°28'20"

IV. References

1. Hausmann, E., and E. Slack, P., *Physics,* D. Van Nostrand Co., New York, 1948, pp. 643–653. Description with examples.
2. Preston, Thomas, *The Theory of Light,* Macmillan and Co., Ltd., London, 1929, pp. 99–100. Statement with examples, pp. 152–155, use to determine index of refraction.

See also Snell's Law.

Quantities

Angle	Direction	Light	Reflection
Density	Index of refraction	Propagation	Speed of Light

TRIBOELECTRICITY

I. Description

There is produced an electromotive force between two dissimilar metals, both at the same temperature, by relative motion at the contact point of the two materials. These materials may be liquid or solid.

II. Illustration

This effect has been known to cause difficulties in self-balancing systems, especially when subjected to vibration. The charges built up on automobiles in motion is also due to this cause.

This phenomenon has been used in the design of a metals separator. Xerography, the process of making copies of printed pages and drawings, also depends to some extent on this process.

```
Millivolts +

0  ── 90 Ni-10 Cr (electrode material)

   ── Fe (Pure)

      ── High-speed 18-4-1
1.0   ── Type 446 stainless
      ── 35 Cr-60 Ni

2.0   ── Ni (Pure)

      ── 4 Mn-95 Ni

3.0

      ── 67 Ni-30 Cu

      ── 52 Ni-48 Fe
4.0
```

III. Magnitude

The magnitude of the potentials depends upon the position of the metals in the electromotive series. Normally it may be expected to be one volt or less.

The above graph shows the triboelectric potential developed with a 90% nickel–10% chromium electrode in a practical metal sorter for rapid machine shop identification of stock.

IV. References

1. Seth, J. B., B. Gulata, and S. Singh, "Electromotive Forces Between Two Metals in Relative Motion," *Philosophical Magazine,* Vol. 12, 1931, pp. 409–429.
2. Gemant, Andrew, *Frictional Phenomena,* Chemical Publishing Co., Brooklyn, New York, 1950, pp. 457–460. Mechanism and magnitudes. Good coverage of friction.
3. *Product Engineering,* May, 1947, p. 93. A use of this phenomenon to sort metals, also triboelectric spectra. Product made by Control Equipment Co., Pittsburgh (Metal sorter).

See also Electrokinetic Phenomena, Volta Effect.

Quantities

Charge   Chemical composition   Friction   Potential   Velocity

VOLTA EFFECT

I. Description

When two metals are placed in contact with one another in the air, one becomes positive and the other negative, though the charges are feeble.

II. Illustration

Rectifiers (such as the copper oxide) take advantage of this contact potential. Dry voltic piles have been employed to produce high voltages for very low current applications such as focusing electrodes for infrared image converter tubes.

III. Magnitude

If the two metals are iron and copper, the iron has a potential about 0.15 volt higher than the copper, while for tin and iron the difference is 0.31 volt, the tin being the higher. For tin and copper (above) it is $0.31 + 0.15 = 0.46$ volt; it makes no difference whether the tin and copper are in direct contact, or separated by other intervening metals. The effect is temperature sensitive.

IV. References

1. Elliott, A., "The Dry Voltic Pile," *Electronic Engineering*, London, October, 1948, Vol. 20, No. 248, pp. 317–319. A description of a practical 500-volt pile.

   See also Triboelectricity.

Quantities

Charge   Chemical composition   Potential   Temperature

WEBER-FECHNER LAW

I. Description

The Weber-Fechner law of psychology states that the least change in the stimulus necessary to produce a perceptible change in response is proportional to the stimulus already existing.

II. Illustration

This law forms the basis of the power level measurement used in audio systems. Since the ear finds that changes in sound intensity are in the same ratio as their energies, a change from 20 to 30 milliwatts of acoustic energy will seem to be the same increment as a change from 200 to 300 milliwatts of audiopower. These levels are equally spaced on a logarithmic scale.

III. Magnitude

The common unit used in connection with this law is the decibel (db), and the gain or loss of a system is given by:

$$db = 10 \log \frac{P_1}{P_2}$$

where P_1 and P_2 are the input and output power levels of the system.

All the senses follow this law. The approximate minimum changes discernible are:

Light	1%
Length of lines	2%
Feeling of weight	10%
Sound loudness	30%

IV. References

1. Ware, L. A., and H. R. Reed, *Communication Circuits,* John Wiley and Sons, New York, 3rd Ed., 1949. Decibels.

2. Woodworth, Robert S., *Psychology,* Henry Holt and Co., New York, 1929, pp. 409–412. Errors of perception.

Quantities

Energy (K.E.)	Length	Power	Temperature
Force	Light	Sound	

WIEDEMANN-FRANZ'S LAW

I. Description

The ratio of the thermal to the electrical conductivity for all metals is proportional to the absolute temperature T. The Wiedemann-Franz formula has been derived theoretically and its coefficient involves both the Boltzmann constant and the electronic charge. Lorenz showed that this constant varies with absolute temperature.

II. Illustration

This theoretical law is generally observed in nature, for the better electrical conductors are also the better heat conductors. However, while the thermal and electrical conductors of metals increase at low temperature, their paths are not parallel and the ratio does change.

III. Magnitude

The theoretical formula is:

$$\frac{n}{G} = 3 \left(\frac{k}{e}\right)^2 T$$

where n = thermal conductivity

G = electrical conductivity

e = electron charge = 1.59×10^{-20} emu.

k = Boltzmann constant = 1.37×10^{-16} erg/°K

T = absolute temperature in °K:

$$\frac{n}{G} = 5.99 \text{ emu or } 1.43 \times 10^{-6} \text{ calorie-ohm/sec/°K}$$

The ratio observed for a number of metals:

Platinum	0.00000143 calorie ohm per sec per degree K
Copper	0.00000156 calorie ohm per sec per degree K
Lead	0.00000169 calorie ohm per sec per degree K

For most metals the observed ratio is a little higher than that given by the formula, doubtless because of thermal conduction due to other causes than electronic activity.

IV. Reference

1. Kraus, Charles A., *The Properties of Electrically Conducting Systems,* The Chemical Catalog Company, New York, 1922, pp. 402–4. A short discussion.
2. Page, Leigh, *Introduction to Theoretical Physics,* D. Van Nostrand Co., New York, 1949, p. 455. Theoretical derivation of equations.

Quantities

Chemical composition   Resistivity   Solid   Temperature

WIEN EFFECT

I. Description

The equivalent conductance* of an electrolyte increases with the applied voltage. This means that Ohm's law is invalid for electrolytic solutions. This effect is especially pronounced for the weak organic acids; the weaker the acid, the stronger the effect.

II. Illustration

The Debye and Onsager theory of conductance* explains the Wien effect by the faster ion speeds of 1 meter/sec at high voltages versus 0.001 cm/sec at low voltages. The conductance of the solution will approach a theoretical maximum value at high voltages. This theoretical value is attained at lower voltages for lower concentrations.

III. Magnitude

The Blumentritt equation expresses the Wien effect for voltage gradients up to 30,000 v/cm:

$$\Delta\Lambda = aE^2 - bE^4$$

where $\Delta\Lambda$ = delta change in equivalent conductance*
    a, b = constants
    E = applied voltage

The constants for the Blumentritt equation have been observed for a number of materials:

Salt	Normality, moles/liter	$a \times 10^{11}$	$b \times 10^{11}$	Normality, moles/liter	$a \times 10^{11}$	$b \times 10^{11}$
$MgSO_4$	0.00605	1.49	1.7	0.00127	2.5	6.0
$MgCrO_4$	0.00574	1.21	3.0	0.00126	1.8	7.5
$K_3Fe(CN)_6$	0.00350	0.44	1.1	0.00082	0.77	3.4
$K_4Fe(CN)_6$	0.00363	0.88	2.3	0.00083	0.82	3.8
$Ba_2Fe(CN)_6$	0.00575	6.6	3.2	0.00108	11.6	6.9

* Defined in Kohlrausch's law.

IV. References

1. Dole, Malcolm, *Principles of Experimental and Theoretical Electro-Chemistry*, McGraw-Hill Book Co., New York, 1935, pp. 108–128. Effect, cause, and calculation of magnitude. *See also* Kohlrausch's Law.

Quantities

Concentration   Current   Liquid   Potential   Resistivity

WIEN'S DISPLACEMENT LAW

I. Description

When the temperature of a radiating black body increases, the wavelength corresponding to maximum energy decreases so that the product of the absolute temperature and wavelength is constant. This means that hot bodies radiate more energy at shorter wavelengths than cool ones.

The emissive power of the black body within the maximum intensity wavelength interval $d\lambda$ is proportional to the fifth power of the absolute temperature.

II. Illustration

As the temperature rises the peak of the distribution curve is displaced or shifted toward the short wavelength end of the spectrum. This can be observed when an iron rod is being heated; it glows dull red first, then gets white-hot as its temperature rises. Thus, this principle is used for temperature measurement in an optical pyrometer.

III. Magnitude

The product of the wavelength and temperature remains constant, and is expressed:

$$\lambda_{max} T = C_1$$

where λ_{max} = wavelength in centimeters of peak intensity wavelength

T = temperature, °K

The value of the displacement constant C_1 is about 0.2884 cm degree, differing slightly on the method of computation used.

For a short interval about the intensity peak, the energy content is given by:

$$dE_{max} = C_2 T^5 \, d\lambda$$

The value of C_2 is about 1.302 × 10⁻⁴ erg/cm³ sec degree⁵ as established by Planck, and the distribution of the radiation intensity is:

$$\psi_\lambda = C_1 \lambda^{-5} \epsilon^{-C_2/\lambda T}$$

where ψ_λ = intensity at wavelength λ

IV. Reference

1. Richtmyer, F. K., and E. H. Kennard, *Introduction to Modern Physics,* McGraw-Hill Book Co., New York, 5th Ed., 1949, pp. 157–8. Derivation of the law, also differences in the value of C_1.

See also Stefan-Boltzmann Law.

Quantities

Emissivity	Intensity	Radiation
Frequency	Light	Temperature

WOOD AND ELLETT EFFECT

I. Description

The almost complete plane polarization of the resonance radiation of mercury vapor for the 2537 A line is completely removed by the action of weak magnetic fields. For both mercury and sodium vapor, magnetic fields may destroy polarization if initially present, and produce it if it is initially absent.

II. Illustration

For mercury vapor, this effect is observable only when the vapor pressure is low so as to suppress the unpolarized resonance radiation. The relation of the directions of the magnetic field, plane of incident light polarization, and the plane of viewing is important, in that the angles between them determine the plane of polarization of the observed light, or even whether it will be polarized at all.

III. Magnitude

Magnetic fields of as low an intensity as that of the earth are sufficient to destroy polarization in mercury vapor, although the maximum effect occurs for intensities of 2 to 3 gauss for mercury and 80 to 100 gauss for sodium. For alternating magnetic field, this depolarizing action decreases with increasing frequency, disappearing at about 5 mc.

IV. Reference

1. Wood, Robert W., *Physical Optics,* The Macmillan Co., New York, 3rd Ed., 1934, pp. 718–728. Effect, cause, and related magneto-optical effects.

See also Luminescence.

Quantities

Frequency	Magnetic flux	Radiation
Light	Polarization	Vapor pressure

ZEEMAN EFFECT

(Also called
Lorentz-Thomson-Zeeman effect
Paschen-Bock effect)

I. Description

When a source having strong line spectra is placed in a strong magnetic field, the lines of the spectrum are widened and many spectral
lines may be broken into multiple lines.

The edges of the broadened line show traces of circular or plane
polarization, depending on whether the observation is made along or
at right angles to the lines of magnetic force.

When the light is examined in a direction perpendicular to the
lines of force, the edges are found to be plane-polarized. With a sufficiently strong field the line will appear triple. The two outer components are polarized with their vibration directions perpendicular
to the lines of force. The pattern changes with strong and weak fields,
the change being known as the Paschen-Bock effect.

II. Illustration

When a source of light, such as a metallic arc, is placed between the
poles of a powerful electromagnet, the lines of its spectrum are split
into components, some displaced to the red and some to the blue, and

each of these two is polarized in a characteristic way. This is a means of discovering the nature of the forces in the atom.

III. Magnitude

In a magnetic field of 30,000 gauss, the extreme components into which a line is split are never more than about 1 A apart, and there may be more than a dozen components between them, so that it is not only necessary to have a powerful magnet but also a spectroscope of high-resolving power.

IV. References

1. Richtmyer, F. K., E. H. Kennard, and T. Lauritsen, *Introduction to Modern Physics,* McGraw-Hill Book Co., New York, 5th Ed., 1955. Pp. 75–80, effect and explanation; pp. 365–386, normal and anomalous effect, strong and weak fields.
2. Jenkins, F. A. and H. E. White, *Fundamentals of Physical Optics,* McGraw-Hill Book Co., New York, 1950. Fundamental understanding plus relation to Faraday effect, Voigt effect, and others.

See also Wood and Ellett Effect.

Quantities

Color	Light	Polarization
Frequency	Magnetic flux	

ZENER EFFECT

I. Description

When an inverse voltage is applied to a rectifying semi-conductor junction, the current will stay constant (approximately) until the voltage becomes very high. At this time the current increases very rapidly for small voltage increases.

Zener voltage is the maximum voltage which the rectifying junction can support in a blocking direction without this large increase in current.

II. Illustration

This effect is present in germanium and silicon and is thus important in application of rectifiers and transistors. It determines the maximum inverse voltage rating of the rectifier. This effect is temperature sensitive. With silicon it is usable as a voltage reference.

III. Magnitude

The Zener voltage will vary considerably from sample to sample, depending upon the types of impurities employed in the semi-conductor. Voltages up to 400 volts and even 1 to 2,000 have been found on momentary applications. It is more usually about 100 volts. The Zener current is usually several microamperes. The effect may be influenced by the light falling on the semi-conducting junction.

IV. Reference

1. McAfee, K. B., E. J. Ryder, W. Shockley, and M. Sparks, "Observations of Zener Current in Germanium P-N Junctions" *Physics Review*, Vol. 83, p. 650, August 1, 1951.

Quantities

Area	Current	Potential	Resistivity
Chemical composition	Light	Radiation	Temperature

Cross Reference
by Physical Quantities

ABSORPTION

Absorption (Absorption, Amplitude, Chemical Composition, Color, Energy (K.E.), Frequency, Light)

Compton Effect (Absorption, Dispersion, Frequency, Radiation)

Lambert's Law (Absorption, Chemical Composition, Frequency, Length, Light, Liquid, Radiation)

Luminescence (Absorption, Chemical Composition, Color, Emissivity, Energy (K.E.), Intensity, Light, Magnetic Flux, Radiation, Temperature)

Stefan-Boltzmann Law (Absorption, Emissivity, Frequency, Light, Radiation, Temperature)

Stokes's Law of Fluorescence (Absorption, Chemical Composition, Color, Emissivity, Energy (K.E.), Frequency, Intensity, Light)

ACCELERATION

Bremstrahlung Radiation (Acceleration, Density, Electric Flux, Energy (K.E.), Frequency, Potential, Radiation)

Kepler's Laws (Acceleration, Area, Force, Length, Time)

Newton's Laws (Acceleration, Direction, Force, Mass, Velocity)

AMPLITUDE

Absorption (Absorption, Amplitude, Chemical Composition, Color, Energy (K.E.), Frequency, Light)

Magnetostriction and Allied Effects (Amplitude, Angle, Coefficient of Expansion, Current, Force, Frequency, Length, Magnetic Flux, Permeability, Sound, Stress, Temperature)

236

ANGLE

Ampère's Law (Angle, Charge, Current, Force, Length, Magnetic Flux, Potential, Velocity)

Ampère's (Biot-Savart) Law (Angle, Current, Length, Magnetic Flux)

Brewster's Law (Angle, Index of Refraction, Polarization)

Cosmic Rays (Angle, Concentration, Direction, Energy (K.E.), Position, Radiation)

Diffraction (Angle, Color, Diffraction, Frequency, Length, Light, Radiation, Sound)

Faraday Effect (Angle, Chemical Composition, Frequency, Index of Refraction, Length, Light, Magnetic Flux, Polarization, Temperature)

Galvanomagnetic and Thermomagnetic Effects (Angle, Chemical Composition, Current, Heat Flux, Magnetic Flux, Temperature)

Gauss's Law (Angle, Area, Charge, Dielectric Constant, Electric Flux, Length, Magnetic Flux, Permeability)

Gladstone and Dale's Law (Angle, Chemical Composition, Color, Density, Index of Refraction, Strain, Temperature)

Kerr Effect (Electrostatic) (Angle, Chemical Composition, Electric Flux, Frequency, Light, Opaqueness, Polarization, Time, Translucence)

Kerr Magneto-Optic Effect (Angle, Chemical Composition, Color, Light, Magnetic Flux, Polarization, Reflection)

Magnetostriction and Allied Effects (Amplitude, Angle, Coefficient of Expansion, Current, Force, Frequency, Length, Magnetic Flux, Permeability, Sound, Stress, Temperature)

Optical Rotary Power (Angle, Chemical Composition, Concentration, Frequency, Length, Light, Polarization)

Snell's Law (Angle, Density, Frequency, Index of Refraction, Light, Magnification, Molecular Weight, Speed of Light, Temperature)

Total Reflection (Angle, Density, Direction, Index of Refraction, Light, Propagation, Reflection, Speed of Light)

AREA

Biot and Fourier's Law (Area, Heat Flux, Temperature, Time)

Fick's Laws (Area, Chemical Composition, Concentration, Liquid, Potential, Temperature, Time)

Gauss's Law (Angle, Area, Charge, Dielectric Constant, Electric Flux, Length, Magnetic Flux, Permeability)

Hooke's Law (Area, Force, Length, Strain, Stress)

Kepler's Laws (Acceleration, Area, Force, Length, Time)

Newton's Law of Heating and Cooling (Area, Conductivity, Film Coefficient, Heat Flux, Mass, Specific Heat, Temperature, Volume)

Pinch Effect (Area, Current, Force, Magnetic Flux, Pressure)

Zener Effect (Area, Chemical Composition, Current, Light, Potential, Radiation, Resistivity, Temperature)

BOILING POINT

Arrhenius Theory of Electrolytic Dissociation (Boiling Point, Chemical Composition, Freezing Point)

Leidenfrost's Phenomena (Boiling Point, Heat Flux, Liquid, Temperature)

State and Change of State (Boiling Point, Chemical Composition, Enthalpy, Freezing Point, Gas, Liquid, Pressure, Solid, Temperature)

BRIGHTNESS—*See* Intensity

CAPACITANCE

Capacitance/Dielectric (Capacitance, Charge, Dielectric Constant, Length, Potential, Temperature)

Ferranti Effect (Capacitance, Frequency, Inductance, Length, Potential, Resistivity)

Ferroelectric Phenomena (Capacitance, Charge, Dielectric Constant, Electric Flux, Polarization, Potential, Temperature)

Impedance/Frequency (Capacitance, Frequency, Inductance)

Lichtenecker's Law (Capacitance, Dielectric Constant)

Ohm's Law (Capacitance, Current, Frequency, Inductance, Potential, Resistivity)

CHARGE

Ampère's Law (Angle, Charge, Current, Force, Length, Magnetic Flux, Potential, Velocity)

Capacitance/Dielectric (Capacitance, Charge, Dielectric Constant, Length, Potential, Temperature)

Conservation Laws (Charge, Energy (K.E.), Energy (P.E.), Light, Mass, Momentum, Sound, Velocity)

Coulomb's Law (Charge, Dielectric Constant, Force, Length, Magnetic Flux, Mass, Permeability)

Ferroelectric Phenomena (Capacitance, Charge, Dielectric Constant, Electric Flux, Polarization, Potential, Temperature)

Gauss's Law (Angle, Area, Charge, Dielectric Constant, Electric Flux, Length, Magnetic Flux, Permeability)

Group Displacement Law (Charge, Chemical Composition, Emissivity, Energy (P.E.), Mass, Radiation, Time)

Hertz Effect (Charge, Current, Light, Radiation)

Piezoelectric Effect (Charge, Force, Frequency, Potential, Strain)

Pyroelectric Effect (Charge, Potential, Temperature)

Radioactivity (Charge, Emissivity, Energy (K.E.), Radiation)

Residual Voltage (Charge, Current, Magnetic Flux, Potential, Time)

Triboelectricity (Charge, Chemical Composition, Friction, Potential, Velocity)

Volta Effect (Charge, Chemical Composition, Potential, Temperature)

CHEMICAL COMPOSITION

Absorption (Absorption, Amplitude, Chemical Composition, Color, Energy (K.E.), Frequency, Light)

Adsorption (Chemical Composition, Concentration, Gas, Surface Tension)

Arrhenius Theory of Electrolytic Dissociation (Boiling Point, Chemical Composition, Freezing Point)

Constant Heat Capacity Law (Chemical Composition, Specific Heat, Temperature)

Corbino Effect (Chemical Composition, Current, Length, Magnetic Flux)

Curie-Weiss Law (Chemical Composition, Magnetic Flux, Permeability, Temperature)

Debye Frequency Effect (Chemical Composition, Concentration, Current, Frequency, Resistivity)

Elastic Limit (Chemical Composition, Strain, Stress)

Electrokinetic Phenomena (Chemical Composition, Current, Direction, Flow, Potential, Pressure)

Faraday Effect (Angle, Chemical Composition, Frequency, Index of Refraction, Length, Light, Magnetic Flux, Polarization, Temperature)

Faraday's Law of Electrolysis (Chemical Composition, Concentration, Current, Energy (P.E), Mass, Molecular Weight, Potential, Resistivity)

Fick's Laws (Area, Chemical Composition, Concentration, Liquid, Potential, Temperature, Time)

Galvanomagnetic and Thermomagnetic Effects (Angle, Chemical Composition, Current, Heat Flux, Magnetic Flux, Temperature)

Geiger-Nuttal Rule (Chemical Composition, Energy (K.E.), Length, Radiation, Time, Velocity)

Gladstone and Dale's Law (Angle, Chemical Composition, Color, Density, Index of Refraction, Strain, Temperature)

Graham's Law (Chemical Composition, Concentration, Flow, Gas, Liquid, Pressure, Temperature, Time)

Group Displacement Law (Charge, Chemical Composition, Emissivity, Energy (P.E.), Mass, Radiation, Time)

Henry's Law (Chemical Composition, Gas, Liquid, Mass, Pressure, Temperature Volume)

Johnson-Rahbek and/or Winslow Effect (Chemical Composition, Electric Flux, Friction, Liquid, Potential)

Kerr Effect (Electrostatic) (Angle, Chemical Composition, Electric Flux, Frequency, Light, Opaqueness, Polarization, Time, Translucence)

Kerr Magneto-Optic Effect (Angle, Chemical Composition, Color, Light, Magnetic Flux, Polarization, Reflection)

Kohlrausch's Law (Chemical Composition, Concentration, Current, Dielectric Constant, Resistivity, Temperature)

Lambert's Law (Absorption, Chemical Composition, Frequency, Length, Light, Liquid, Radiation)

Liquid Crystal Phase (Chemical Composition, Diffraction, Light, Liquid, Opaqueness, Temperature, Translucence)

Luminescence (Absorption, Chemical Composition, Color, Emissivity, Energy (K.E.), Intensity, Light, Magnetic Flux, Radiation, Temperature)

Magnetic Behavior of Materials (Chemical Composition, Magnetic Flux)

Optical Rotary Power (Angle, Chemical Composition, Concentration, Frequency, Length, Light, Polarization)

Paschen's Law (Chemical Composition, Gas, Length, Potential, Pressure)

Periodic Law (Chemical Composition, Radiation)

Photoelectric Effect (Chemical Composition, Energy (K.E.), Frequency, Intensity, Light, Polarization, Potential, Speed of Light)

Resistance/Pressure Effect (Chemical Composition, Pressure, Resistivity)

Resistance/Temperature (Chemical Composition, Resistivity, Temperature)

Richardson's Effect (Chemical Composition, Current, Emissivity, Temperature)

State and Change of State (Boiling Point, Chemical Composition, Enthalpy, Freezing Point, Gas, Liquid, Pressure, Solid, Temperature)

Stokes's Law of Fluorescence (Absorption, Chemical Composition, Color, Emissivity, Energy (K.E.), Frequency, Intensity, Light)

Stress and Strain Effects (Chemical Composition, Force, Frequency, Length, Light, Polarization, Strain, Stress, Temperature, Time, Volume, Yield Point)

Thermoelectric Effects (Chemical Composition, Conductivity, Current, Direction, Force, Heat Flux, Potential, Temperature)

Triboelectricity (Charge, Chemical Composition, Friction, Potential, Velocity)

Volta Effect (Charge, Chemical Composition, Potential, Temperature)

Weidemann-Franz's Law (Chemical Composition, Resistivity, Solid, Temperature)

Zener Effect (Area, Chemical Composition, Current, Light, Potential, Radiation, Resistivity, Temperature)

COEFFICIENT OF EXPANSION

Expansion-Temperature (Coefficient of Expansion, Length, Temperature, Volume)

Magneto-Striction and Allied Effects (Amplitude, Angle, Coefficient of Expansion, Current, Force, Frequency, Length, Magnetic Flux, Permeability, Sound, Stress, Temperature)

COLOR

Absorption (Absorption, Amplitude, Chemical Composition, Color, Energy (K.E.), Frequency, Light)

Christiansen Effect (Color, Frequency, Light, Opaqueness, Temperature, Translucence)

Diffraction (Angle, Color, Diffraction, Frequency, Length, Light, Radiation, Sound)

Gladstone and Dale's Law (Angle, Chemical Composition, Color, Density, Index of Refraction, Strain, Temperature)

Kerr Magneto-Optic Effect (Angle, Chemical Composition, Color, Light, Magnetic Flux, Polarization, Reflection)

Luminescence (Absorption, Chemical Composition, Color, Emissivity, Energy (K.E.), Intensity, Light, Magnetic Flux, Radiation, Temperature)

Purkinje Effect (Color, Intensity, Light)

Stokes's Law of Fluorescence (Absorption, Chemical Composition, Color, Emissivity, Energy (K.E.), Frequency, Intensity, Light)

Zeeman Effect (Color, Frequency, Light, Magnetic Flux, Polarization)

CONCENTRATION

Adsorption (Chemical Composition, Concentration, Gas, Surface Tension)

Cosmic Rays (Angle, Concentration, Direction, Energy (K.E.), Position, Radiation)

Debye Frequency Effect (Chemical Composition, Concentration, Current, Frequency, Resistivity)

Faraday's Law of Electrolysis (Chemical Composition, Concentration, Current, Energy (P.E.), Mass, Molecular Weight, Potential, Resistivity)

Fick's Laws (Area, Chemical Composition, Concentration, Liquid, Potential, Temperature, Time)

Gibbs Theory of Equilibria (Concentration, Pressure, Temperature)

Graham's Law (Chemical Composition, Concentration, Flow, Gas, Liquid, Pressure, Temperature, Time)

Kohlrausch's Law (Chemical Composition, Concentration, Current, Dielectric Constant, Resistivity, Temperature)

Le Châtelier's Law (Concentration, Pressure, Stress, Temperature, Volume)

Optical Rotary Power (Angle, Chemical Composition, Concentration, Frequency, Length, Light, Polarization)

Raoult's Law (Concentration, Gas, Liquid, Molecular Weight, Solid, Temperature, Vapor Pressure)

Surface Tension (Concentration, Force, Length, Liquid, Pressure, Surface Tension, Temperature)

Wien Effect (Concentration, Current, Liquid, Potential, Resistivity)

CONDUCTIVITY

Newton's Law of Heating and Cooling (Area, Conductivity, Film Coefficient, Heat Flux, Mass, Specific Heat, Temperature, Volume)

Thermoelectric Effects (Chemical Composition, Conductivity, Current, Direction, Force, Heat Flux, Potential, Temperature)

CURRENT

Ampère's Law (Angle, Charge, Current, Force, Length, Magnetic Flux, Potential, Velocity)

Ampère's (Biot-Savart) Law (Angle, Current, Length, Magnetic Flux)

Corbino Effect (Chemical Composition, Current, Length, Magnetic Flux)

Debye Frequency Effect (Chemical Composition, Concentration, Current, Frequency, Resistivity)

Electrocapillarity (Current, Flow, Force, Potential, Pressure, Surface Tension)

Electrokinetic Phenomena (Chemical Composition, Current, Direction, Flow, Potential, Pressure)

Faraday's Law of Electrolysis (Chemical Composition, Concentration, Current, Energy (P.E.), Mass, Molecular Weight, Potential, Resistivity)

Faraday's Law of Induction (Current, Energy (P.E.), Inductance, Length, Magnetic Flux, Potential, Time, Velocity)

Galvanomagnetic and Thermomagnetic Effects (Angle, Chemical Composition, Current, Heat Flux, Magnetic Flux, Temperature)

Hertz Effect (Charge, Current, Light, Radiation)

Joule's Law (Current, Energy (K.E.), Heat Flux, Potential, Power, Resistivity, Time)

Kirchhoff's Laws (Current, Potential)

Kohlrausch's Law (Chemical Composition, Concentration, Current, Dielectric Constant, Resistivity, Temperature)

Magnetic Dispersion of Sound (Current, Density, Frequency, Magnetic Flux, Permeability, Resistivity, Sound, Transmission (Speed of Sound))

Magnetic Effects (Current, Direction, Intensity, Length, Light, Magnetic Flux, Permeability, Resistivity)

Magnetostriction and Allied Effects (Amplitude, Angle, Coefficient of Expansion, Current, Force, Frequency, Length, Magnetic Flux, Permeability, Sound, Stress, Temperature)

Ohm's Law (Capacitance, Current, Frequency, Inductance, Potential, Resistivity)

Pinch Effect (Area, Current, Force, Magnetic Flux, Pressure)

Proximity Effect (Current, Frequency, Length, Resistivity)

Residual Voltage (Charge, Current, Magnetic Flux, Potential, Time)

Richardson's Effect (Chemical Composition, Current, Emissivity, Temperature)

Shot Effect (Current, Emissivity, Potential, Sound, Temperature)

Skin Effect (Current, Frequency, Inductance, Length, Permeability, Resistivity, Temperature)

Thermoelectric Effects (Chemical Composition, Conductivity, Current, Direction, Force, Heat Flux, Potential, Temperature)

Wien Effect (Concentration, Current, Liquid, Potential, Resistivity)

Zener Effect (Area, Chemical Composition, Current, Light, Potential, Radiation, Resistivity, Temperature)

DENSITY

Archimedes' Principle (Density, Mass, Specific Gravity, Volume)

Bernoulli's Theorem (Density, Energy (K.E.), Energy (P.E.), Flow, Pressure, Velocity)

Bremstrahlung Radiation (Acceleration, Density, Electric Flux, Energy (K.E.), Frequency, Potential, Radiation)

Fluid Flow Effects (Density, Energy (K.E.), Flow, Length, Mass, Pressure, Specific Gravity, Temperature, Transmission (Speed of Sound), Vapor Pressure, Velocity, Viscosity)

Gladstone and Dale's Law (Angle, Chemical Composition, Color, Density, Index of Refraction, Strain, Temperature)

Kelvin's Principle for Fluid Drops (Density, Length, Liquid, Surface Tension, Temperature, Vapor Pressure)

Magnetic Dispersion of Sound (Current, Density, Frequency, Magnetic Flux, Permeability, Resistivity, Sound, Transmission (Speed of Sound))

Snell's Law (Angle, Density, Frequency, Index of Refraction, Light, Magnification, Molecular Weight, Speed of Light, Temperature)

Stokes's Law (Density, Gas, Length, Temperature, Velocity, Viscosity)

Total Reflection (Angle, Density, Direction, Index of Refraction, Light, Propagation, Reflection, Speed of Light)

DIELECTRIC CONSTANT

Capacitance/Dielectric (Capacitance, Charge, Dielectric Constant, Length, Potential, Temperature)

Coulomb's Law (Charge, Dielectric Constant, Force, Length, Magnetic Flux, Mass, Permeability)

Ferroelectric Phenomena (Capacitance, Charge, Dielectric Constant, Electric Flux, Polarization, Potential, Temperature)

Gauss's Law (Angle, Area, Charge, Dielectric Constant, Electric Flux, Length, Magnetic Flux, Permeability)

Kohlrausch's Law (Chemical Composition, Concentration, Current, Dielectric Constant, Resistivity, Temperature)

Lichtenecker's Law (Capacitance, Dielectric Constant)

DIFFRACTION

Diffraction (Angle, Color, Diffraction, Frequency, Length, Light, Radiation, Sound)

Liquid Crystal Phase (Chemical Composition, Diffraction, Light, Liquid, Opaqueness, Temperature, Translucence)

DIRECTION

Cosmic Rays (Angle, Concentration, Direction, Energy (K.E.), Position, Radiation)

Electrokinetic Phenomena (Chemical Composition, Current, Direction, Flow, Potential, Pressure)

Eotvos Effect (Direction, Mass, Position, Velocity)

Magnetic Effects (Current, Direction, Intensity, Length, Light, Magnetic Flux, Permeability, Resistivity)

Newton's Laws (Acceleration, Direction, Force, Mass, Velocity)

Thermoelectric Effects (Chemical Composition, Conductivity, Current, Direction, Force, Heat Flux, Potential, Temperature)

Total Reflection (Angle, Density, Direction, Index of Refraction, Light, Propagation, Reflection, Speed of Light)

DISPERSION (*also see* DIFFRACTION)

Compton Effect (Absorption, Dispersion, Frequency, Radiation)

ELECTRIC FLUX

Bremstrahlung Radiation (Acceleration, Density, Electric Flux, Energy (K.E.), Frequency, Potential, Radiation)

Ferroelectric Phenomena (Capacitance, Charge, Dielectric Constant, Electric Flux, Polarization, Potential, Temperatures)

Gauss's Law (Angle, Area, Charge, Dielectric Constant, Electric Flux, Length, Magnetic Flux, Permeability)

Johnson-Rahbek and/or Winslow Effect (Chemical Composition, Electric Flux, Friction, Liquid, Potential)

Kerr Effect (Electrostatic) (Angle, Chemical Composition, Electric Flux, Frequency, Light, Opaqueness, Polarization, Time, Translucence)

Stark Effect (Electric Flux, Emissivity, Frequency, Light)

EMISSIVITY

Fission (Emissivity, Energy (K.E.), Energy (P.E.), Radiation)

Group Displacement Law (Charge, Chemical Composition, Emissivity, Energy (P.E.), Mass, Radiation, Time)

Luminescence (Absorption, Chemical Composition, Color, Emissivity, Energy (K.E.), Intensity, Light, Magnetic Flux, Radiation, Temperature)

Radioactivity (Charge, Emissivity, Energy (K.E.), Radiation)

Richardson's Effect (Chemical Composition, Current, Emissivity, Temperature)

Shot Effect (Current, Emissivity, Potential, Sound, Temperature)

Stark Effect (Electric Flux, Emissivity, Frequency, Light)

Stefan-Boltzmann Law (Absorption, Emissivity, Frequency, Light, Radiation, Temperature)

Stokes's Law of Fluorescence (Absorption, Chemical Composition, Color, Emissivity, Energy (K.E.), Frequency, Intensity, Light)

Wien's Displacement Law (Emissivity, Frequency, Intensity, Light, Radiation, Temperature)

ENERGY (K.E.)

Absorption (Absorption, Amplitude, Chemical Composition, Color, Energy (K.E.), Frequency, Light)

Bernoulli's Theorem (Density, Energy (K.E.), Energy (P.E.), Flow, Pressure, Velocity)

Bremstrahlung Radiation (Acceleration, Density, Electric Flux, Energy (K.E.), Frequency, Potential, Radiation)

Cavitation (Energy (K.E.), Pressure, Sound, Temperature, Vapor Pressure, Velocity)

Conservation Laws (Charge, Energy (K.E.), Energy (P.E.), Light, Mass, Momentum, Sound, Velocity)

Cosmic Rays (Angle, Concentration, Direction, Energy (K.E.), Position, Radiation)

Fission (Emissivity, Energy (K.E.), Energy (P.E.), Radiation)

Fluid Flow Effects (Density, Energy (K.E.), Flow, Length, Mass, Pressure, Specific Gravity, Temperature, Transmission (Speed of Sound), Vapor Pressure, Velocity, Viscosity)

Geiger-Nuttal Rule (Chemical Composition, Energy (K.E.), Length, Radiation, Time, Velocity)

Joule's Law (Current, Energy (K.E.), Heat Flux, Potential, Power, Resistivity, Time)

Joule-Thomson Effect (Energy (K.E.), Enthalpy, Gas, Heat Flux, Pressure, Temperature, Volume)

Luminescence (Absorption, Chemical Composition, Color, Emissivity, Energy (K.E.), Intensity, Light, Magnetic Flux, Radiation, Temperature)

Photoelectric Effect (Chemical Composition, Energy (K.E.), Frequency, Intensity, Light, Polarization, Potential, Speed of Light)

Quantum Theory (Energy (K.E.), Frequency, Radiation, Speed of Light, Temperature)

Radioactivity (Charge, Emissivity, Energy (K.E.), Radiation)

Stokes's Law of Fluorescence (Absorption, Chemical Composition, Color, Emissivity, Energy (K.E.), Frequency, Intensity, Light)

Thermodynamic Laws (Energy (K.E.), Energy (P.E.), Enthalpy, Entropy, Heat Flux, Power, Pressure, Temperature)

Weber-Fechner Law (Energy (K.E.), Force, Length, Light, Power, Sound, Temperature)

ENERGY (P.E.)

Bernoulli's Theorem (Density, Energy (K.E.), Energy (P.E.), Flow, Pressure, Velocity)

Conservation Laws (Charge, Energy (K.E), Energy (P.E.), Light, Mass, Momentum, Sound, Velocity)

Faraday's Law of Electrolysis (Chemical Composition, Concentration, Current, Energy (P.E.), Mass, Molecular Weight, Potential, Resistivity)

Faraday's Law of Induction (Current, Energy (P.E.), Inductance, Length, Magnetic Flux, Potential, Time, Velocity)

Fission (Emissivity, Energy (K.E.), Energy (P.E.), Radiation)

Group Displacement Law (Charge, Chemical Composition, Emissivity, Energy (P.E.), Mass, Radiation, Time)

Schrodinger's Wave Equation (Energy (P.E.), Frequency, Mass, Propagation, Time, Velocity)

Thermodynamic Laws (Energy (K.E.), Energy (P.E.), Enthalpy, Entropy, Heat Flux, Power, Pressure, Temperature)

ENTHALPY

Joule-Thomson Effect (Energy (K.E.), Enthalpy, Gas, Heat Flux, Pressure, Temperature, Volume)

State and Change of State (Boiling Point, Chemical Composition, Enthalpy, Freezing Point, Gas, Liquid, Pressure, Solid, Temperature)

Thermodynamic Laws (Energy (K. E.), Energy (P.E.), Enthalpy, Entropy, Heat Flux, Power, Pressure, Temperature)

ENTROPY

Thermodynamic Laws (Energy (K.E.), Energy (P.E.), Enthalpy, Entropy, Heat Flux, Power, Pressure, Temperature)

FILM COEFFICIENT

Newton's Law of Heating and Cooling (Area, Conductivity, Film Coefficient, Heat Flux, Mass, Specific Heat, Temperature, Volume)

FLOW

Bernoulli's Theorem (Density, Energy (K.E.), Energy (P.E.), Flow, Pressure, Velocity)

Electrocapillarity (Current, Flow, Force, Potential, Pressure, Surface Tension)

Electrokinetic Phenomena (Chemical Composition, Current, Direction, Flow, Potential, Pressure)

Fluid Flow Effects (Density, Energy (K.E.), Flow, Length, Mass, Pressure, Specific Gravity, Temperature, Transmission (Speed of Sound), Vapor Pressure, Velocity, Viscosity)

Graham's Law (Chemical Composition, Concentration, Flow, Gas, Liquid, Pressure, Temperature, Time)

FORCE

Ampère's Law (Angle, Charge, Current, Force, Length, Magnetic Flux, Potential, Velocity)

Bauschinger Effect (Force, Length, Strain, Stress, Temperature, Yield Point)

Coulomb's Law (Charge, Dielectric Constant, Force, Length, Magnetic Flux, Mass, Permeability)

Electrocapillarity (Current, Flow, Force, Potential, Pressure, Surface Tension)

Friction Effects (Force, Friction, Strain, Stress, Velocity, Viscosity)

Hooke's Law (Area, Force, Length, Strain, Stress)

Kepler's Laws (Acceleration, Area, Force, Length, Time)

Magnetostriction and Allied Effects (Amplitude, Angle, Coefficient of Expansion, Current, Force, Frequency, Length, Magnetic Flux, Permeability, Sound, Stress, Temperature)

Memory Metals (Force, Heat Flux, Length, Strain, Stress, Temperature)

Newton's Laws (Acceleration, Direction, Force, Mass, Velocity)

Piezoelectric Effect (Charge, Force, Frequency, Potential, Strain)

Pinch Effect (Area, Current, Force, Magnetic Flux, Pressure)

Poisson's Coefficient (Force, Length, Strain, Volume)

Stress and Strain Effects (Chemical Composition, Force, Frequency, Length, Light, Polarization, Strain, Stress, Temperature, Time, Volume, Yield Point)

Surface Tension (Concentration, Force, Length, Liquid, Pressure, Surface Tension, Temperature)

Thermoelastic Effect (Force, Potential, Strain, Stress, Temperature)

Thermoelectric Effect (Chemical Composition, Conductivity, Current, Direction, Force, Heat Flux, Potential, Temperature)

Weber-Fechner Law (Energy (K.E.), Force, Length, Light, Power, Sound, Temperature)

FREEZING POINT

Arrhenius Theory of Electrolytic Dissociation (Boiling Point, Chemical Composition, Freezing Point)

State and Change of State (Boiling Point, Chemical Composition, Enthalpy, Freezing Point, Gas, Liquid, Pressure, Solid, Temperature)

FREQUENCY

Absorption (Absorption, Amplitude, Chemical Composition, Color, Energy (K.E.), Frequency, Light)

Bremstrahlung Radiation (Acceleration, Density, Electric Flux, Energy (K.E.), Frequency, Potential, Radiation)

Christiansen Effect (Color, Frequency, Light, Opaqueness, Temperature, Translucence)

Compton Effect (Absorption, Dispersion, Frequency, Radiation)

Debye Frequency Effect (Chemical Composition, Concentration, Current, Frequency, Resistivity)

Diffraction (Angle, Color, Diffraction, Frequency, Length, Light, Radiation, Sound)

Doppler-Fizeau Effect (Frequency, Light, Radiation, Reflection, Sound, Velocity)

Faraday Effect (Angle, Chemical Composition, Frequency, Index of Refraction, Length, Light, Magnetic Flux, Polarization, Temperature)

Ferranti Effect (Capacitance, Frequency, Inductance, Length, Potential, Resistivity)

Impedance/Frequency (Capacitance, Frequency, Inductance)

Interference (Frequency, Length, Light, Radiation, Sound)

Kerr Effect (Electrostatic) (Angle, Chemical Composition, Electric Flux, Frequency, Light, Opaqueness, Polarization, Time, Translucence)

Lambert's Law (Absorption, Chemical Composition, Frequency, Length, Light, Liquid, Radiation)

Magnetic Dispersion of Sound (Current, Density, Frequency, Magnetic Flux, Permeability, Resistivity, Sound, Transmission (Speed of Sound))

Magnetostriction and Allied Effects (Amplitude, Angle, Coefficient of Expansion, Current, Force, Frequency, Length, Magnetic Flux, Permeability, Sound, Stress, Temperature)

Ohm's Law (Capacitance, Current, Frequency, Inductance, Potential, Resistivity)

Optical Rotary Power (Angle, Chemical Composition, Concentration, Frequency, Length, Light, Polarization)

Organ Pipe Resonance (Frequency, Gas, Length, Resonance, Sound)

Photoelectric Effect (Chemical Composition, Energy (K.E.), Frequency, Intensity, Light, Polarization, Potential, Speed of Light)

Piezoelectric Effect (Charge, Force, Frequency, Potential, Strain)

Proximity Effect (Current, Frequency, Length, Resistivity)

Quantum Theory (Energy (K.E.), Frequency, Radiation, Speed of Light, Temperature)

Schrodinger's Wave Equation (Energy (P.E.), Frequency, Mass, Propagation, Time, Velocity)

Skin Effect (Current, Frequency, Inductance, Length, Permeability, Resistivity, Temperature)

Snell's Law (Angle, Density, Frequency, Index of Refraction, Light, Magnification, Molecular Weight, Speed of Light, Temperature)

Stark Effect (Electric Flux, Emissivity, Frequency, Light)

Stefan-Boltzmann Law (Absorption, Emissivity, Frequency, Light, Radiation, Temperature)

Stokes's Law of Fluorescence (Absorption, Chemical Composition, Color, Emissivity, Energy (K.E.), Frequency, Intensity, Light)

Stress and Strain Effects (Chemical Composition, Force, Frequency, Length, Light, Polarization, Strain, Stress, Temperature, Time, Volume, Yield Point)

Wien's Displacement Law (Emissivity, Frequency, Intensity, Light, Radiation, Temperature)

Wood and Ellett Effect (Frequency, Light, Magnetic Flux, Polarization, Radiation, Vapor Pressure)

Zeeman Effect (Color, Frequency, Light, Magnetic Flux, Polarization)

FRICTION

Friction Effects (Force, Friction, Strain, Stress, Velocity, Viscosity)

Johnson-Rahbek and/or Winslow Effect (Chemical Composition, Electric Flux, Friction, Liquid, Potential)

Triboelectricity (Charge, Chemical Composition, Friction, Potential, Velocity)

GAS

Adsorption (Chemical Composition, Concentration, Gas, Surface Tension)

Graham's Law (Chemical Composition, Concentration, Flow, Gas, Liquid, Pressure, Temperature, Time)

Henry's Law (Chemical Composition, Gas, Liquid, Mass, Pressure, Temperature, Volume)

Ideal Gas Laws (Gas, Mass, Pressure, Temperature, Volume)

Joule-Thomson Effect (Energy (K.E.), Enthalpy, Gas, Heat Flux, Pressure, Temperature, Volume)

Organ Pipe Resonance (Frequency, Gas, Length, Resonance, Sound)

Paschen's Law (Chemical Composition, Gas, Length, Potential, Pressure)

Raoult's Law (Concentration, Gas, Liquid, Molecular Weight, Solid, Temperature, Vapor Pressure)

State and Change of State (Boiling Point, Chemical Composition, Enthalpy, Freezing Point, Gas, Liquid, Pressure, Solid, Temperature)

Stokes's Law (Density, Gas, Length, Temperature, Velocity, Viscosity)

HEAT—*see* HEAT FLUX

HEAT FLUX

Biot and Fourier's Law (Area, Heat Flux, Temperature, Time)

Galvanomagnetic and Thermomagnetic Effects (Angle, Chemical Composition, Current, Heat Flux, Magnetic Flux, Temperature)

Joule's Law (Current, Energy (K.E.), Heat Flux, Potential, Power, Resistivity, Time)

Joule-Thomson Effect (Energy (K.E.), Enthalpy, Gas, Heat Flux, Pressure, Temperature, Volume)

Leidenfrost's Phenomena (Boiling Point, Heat Flux, Liquid, Temperature)

Memory Metals (Force, Heat Flux, Length, Strain, Stress, Temperature)

Newton's Law of Heating and Cooling (Area, Conductivity, Film Coefficient, Heat Flux, Mass, Specific Heat, Temperature, Volume)

Thermodynamic Laws (Energy (K.E.), Energy (P.E.), Enthalpy, Entropy, Heat Flux, Pressure, Temperature)

Thermoelectric Effects (Chemical Composition, Conductivity, Current, Direction, Force, Heat Flux, Potential, Temperature)

INDEX OF REFRACTION

Brewster's Law (Angle, Index of Refraction, Polarization)

Faraday Effect (Angle, Chemical Composition, Frequency, Index of Refraction, Length, Light, Magnetic Flux, Polarization, Temperature)

Gladstone and Dale's Law (Angle, Chemical Composition, Color, Density, Index of Refraction, Strain, Temperature)

Snell's Law (Angle, Density, Frequency, Index of Refraction, Light, Magnification, Molecular Weight, Speed of Light, Temperature)

Total Reflection (Angle, Density, Direction, Index of Refraction, Light, Propagation, Reflection, Speed of Light)

INDUCTANCE

Barkhausen Effect (Inductance, Magnetic Flux, Permeability, Sound)

Faraday's Law of Induction (Current, Energy (P.E.), Inductance, Length, Magnetic Flux, Potential, Time, Velocity)

Ferranti Effect (Capacitance, Frequency, Inductance, Length, Potential, Resistivity)

Impedance/Frequency (Capacitance, Frequency, Inductance)

Ohm's Law (Capacitance, Current, Frequency, Inductance, Potential, Resistivity)

Skin Effect (Current, Frequency, Inductance, Length, Permeability, Resistivity, Temperature)

INTENSITY

Luminescence (Absorption, Chemical Composition, Color, Emissivity, Energy (K.E.), Intensity, Light, Magnetic Flux, Radiation, Temperature)

Magnetic Effects (Current, Direction, Intensity, Length, Light, Magnetic Flux Permeability, Resistivity)

Photoelectric Effect (Chemical Composition, Energy (K.E.), Frequency, Intensity, Light, Polarization, Potential, Speed of Light)

Purkinje Effect (Color, Intensity, Light)

Stokes's Law of Fluorescence (Absorption, Chemical Composition, Color, Emissivity, Energy (K.E.), Frequency, Intensity, Light)

Wien's Displacement Law (Emissivity, Frequency, Intensity, Light, Radiation, Temperature)

LENGTH

Ampère's Law (Angle, Charge, Current, Force, Length, Magnetic Flux, Potential, Velocity)

Ampère's (Biot-Savart) Law (Angle, Current, Length, Magnetic Flux)

Bauschinger Effect (Force, Length, Strain, Stress, Temperature, Yield Point)

Capacitance/Dielectric (Capacitance, Charge, Dielectric Constant, Length, Potential, Temperature)

Corbino Effect (Chemical Composition, Current, Length, Magnetic Flux)

Coulomb's Law (Charge, Dielectric Constant, Force, Length, Magnetic Flux, Mass, Permeability)

Diffraction (Angle, Color, Diffraction, Frequency, Length, Light, Radiation, Sound)

Expansion/Temperature (Coefficient of Expansion, Length, Temperature, Volume)

Faraday Effect (Angle, Chemical Composition, Frequency, Index of Refraction, Length, Light, Magnetic Flux, Polarization, Temperature)

Faraday's Law of Induction (Current, Energy (P.E.), Inductance, Length, Magnetic Flux, Potential, Time, Velocity)

Ferranti Effect (Capacitance, Frequency, Inductance, Length, Potential, Resistivity)

Fluid Flow Effects (Density, Energy (K.E.), Flow, Length, Mass, Pressure, Specific Gravity, Temperature, Transmission (Speed of Sound), Vapor Pressure, Velocity, Viscosity)

Gauss's Law (Angle, Area, Charge, Dielectric Constant, Electric Flux, Length, Magnetic Flux, Permeability)

Geiger-Nuttal Rule (Chemical Composition, Energy (K.E.), Length, Radiation, Time, Velocity)

Hooke's Law (Area, Force, Length, Strain, Stress)

Interference (Frequency, Length, Light, Radiation, Sound)

Kelvin's Principle for Fluid Drops (Density, Length, Liquid, Surface Tension, Temperature, Vapor Pressure)

Kepler's Laws (Acceleration, Area, Force, Length, Time)

Lambert's Law (Absorption, Chemical Composition, Frequency, Length, Light, Liquid, Radiation)

Magnetic Effects (Current, Direction, Intensity, Length, Light, Magnetic Flux, Permeability, Resistivity)

Magnetostriction and Allied Effects (Amplitude, Angle, Coefficient of Expansion, Current, Force, Frequency, Length, Magnetic Flux, Permeability, Sound, Stress, Temperature)

Memory Metals (Force, Heat Flux, Length, Strain, Stress, Temperature)

Optical Rotary Power (Angle, Chemical Composition, Concentration, Frequency, Length, Light, Polarization)

Organ Pipe Resonance (Frequency, Gas, Length, Resonance, Sound)

Paschen's Law (Chemical Composition, Gas, Length, Potential, Pressure)

Poisson's Coefficient (Force, Length, Strain, Volume)

Proximity Effect (Current, Frequency, Length, Resistivity)

Resistance/Dimension (Length, Resistivity, Strain)

Skin Effect (Current, Frequency, Inductance, Length, Permeability, Resistivity, Temperature)

Stokes's Law (Density, Gas, Length, Temperature, Velocity, Viscosity)

Stress and Strain Effects (Chemical Composition, Force, Frequency, Length, Light, Polarization, Strain, Stress, Temperature, Time, Volume, Yield Point)

Surface Tension (Concentration, Force, Length, Liquid, Pressure, Surface Tension, Temperature)

Weber-Fechner Law (Energy (K.E.), Force, Length, Light, Power, Sound, Temperature)

LIGHT (*see also* RADIATION)

Absorption (Absorption, Amplitude, Chemical Composition, Color, Energy (K.E.), Frequency, Light)

Christiansen Effect (Color, Frequency, Light, Opaqueness, Temperature, Translucence)

Conservation Laws (Charge, Energy (K.E.), Energy (P.E.), Light, Mass, Momentum, Sound, Velocity)

Diffraction (Angle, Color, Diffraction, Frequency, Length, Light, Radiation, Sound)

Doppler-Fizeau Effect (Frequency, Light, Radiation, Reflection, Sound, Velocity)

Faraday Effect (Angle, Chemical Composition, Frequency, Index of Refraction, Length, Light, Magnetic Flux, Polarization, Temperature)

Hertz Effect (Charge, Current, Light, Radiation)

Interference (Frequency, Length, Light, Radiation, Sound)

Kerr Effect (Electrostatic) (Angle, Chemical Composition, Electric Flux, Frequency, Light, Opaqueness, Polarization, Time, Translucence)

Kerr Magneto-Optic Effect (Angle, Chemical Composition, Color, Light, Magnetic Flux, Polarization, Reflection)

Lambert's Law (Absorption, Chemical Composition, Frequency, Length, Light, Liquid, Radiation)

Liquid Crystal Phase (Chemical Composition, Diffraction, Light, Liquid, Opaqueness, Temperature, Translucence)

Luminescence (Absorption, Chemical Composition, Color, Emissivity, Energy (K.E.), Intensity, Light, Magnetic Flux, Radiation, Temperature)

Magnetic Effects (Current, Direction, Intensity, Length, Light, Magnetic Flux, Permeability, Resistivity)

Optical Rotary Power (Angle, Chemical Composition, Concentration, Frequency, Length, Light, Polarization)

Photoelectric Effect (Chemical Composition, Energy (K.E.), Frequency, Intensity, Light, Polarization, Potential, Speed of Light)

Photomagnetic Effect (Light, Magnetic Flux, Potential, Radiation)

Purkinje Effect (Color, Intensity, Light)

Radiation Pressure (Light, Pressure, Radiation, Speed of Light)

Snell's Law (Angle, Density, Frequency, Index of Refraction, Light, Magnification, Molecular Weight, Speed of Light, Temperature)

Stark Effect (Electric Flux, Emissivity, Frequency, Light)

Stefan-Boltzmann Law (Absorption, Emissivity, Frequency, Light, Radiation, Temperature)

Stokes's Law of Fluorescence (Absorption, Chemical Composition, Color, Emissivity, Energy (K.E.), Frequency, Intensity, Light)

Stress and Strain Effects (Chemical Composition, Force, Frequency, Length, Light, Polarization, Strain, Stress, Temperature, Time, Volume, Yield Point)

Total Reflection (Angle, Direction, Index of Refraction, Light, Propagation, Reflection, Speed of Light)

Weber-Fechner Law (Energy (K.E.), Force, Length, Light, Power, Sound, Temperature)

Wien's Displacement Law (Emissivity, Frequency, Intensity, Light, Radiation, Temperature)

Wood and Ellett Effect (Frequency, Light, Magnetic Flux, Polarization, Radiation, Vapor Pressure)

Zeeman Effect (Color, Frequency, Light, Magnetic Flux, Polarization)

Zener Effect (Area, Current, Chemical Composition, Light, Potential, Radiation, Resistivity, Temperature)

LIQUID

Fick's Laws (Area, Chemical Composition, Concentration, Liquid, Potential, Temperature, Time)

Graham's Law (Chemical Composition, Concentration, Flow, Gas, Liquid, Pressure, Temperature, Time)

Henry's Law (Chemical Composition, Gas, Liquid, Mass, Pressure, Temperature, Volume)

Johnson-Rahbek and/or Winslow Effect (Chemical Composition, Electric Flux, Friction, Liquid, Potential)

Kelvin's Principle for Fluid Drops (Density, Length, Liquid, Surface Tension, Temperature, Vapor Pressure)

Lambert's Law (Absorption, Chemical Composition, Frequency, Length, Light, Liquid, Radiation)

Leidenfrost's Phenomena (Boiling Point, Heat Flux, Liquid, Temperature)

Liquid Crystal Phase (Chemical Composition, Diffraction, Light, Liquid, Opaqueness, Temperature, Translucence)

Raoult's Law (Concentration, Gas, Liquid, Molecular Weight, Solid, Temperature, Vapor Pressure)

State and Change of State (Boiling Point, Chemical Composition, Enthalpy, Freezing Point, Gas, Liquid, Pressure, Solid, Temperature)

Surface Tension (Concentration, Force, Length, Liquid, Pressure, Surface Tension)

Wien Effect (Concentration, Current, Liquid, Potential, Resistivity)

MAGNETIC FLUX

Ampère's Law (Angle, Charge, Current, Force, Length, Magnetic Flux, Potential, Velocity)

Ampère's (Biot-Savart) Law (Angle, Current, Length, Magnetic Flux)

Barkhausen Effect (Inductance, Magnetic Flux, Permeability, Sound)

Corbino Effect (Chemical Composition, Current, Length, Magnetic Flux)

Coulomb's Law (Charge, Dielectric Constant, Force, Length, Magnetic Flux, Mass, Permeability)

Curie-Weiss Law (Chemical Composition, Magnetic Flux, Permeability, Temperature)

Faraday Effect (Angle, Chemical Composition, Frequency, Index of Refraction, Length, Light, Magnetic Flux, Polarization, Temperature)

Faraday's Law of Induction (Current, Energy (P.E.), Inductance, Length, Magnetic Flux, Potential, Time, Velocity)

Galvanomagnetic and Thermomagnetic Effects (Angle, Chemical Composition, Current, Heat Flux, Magnetic Flux, Temperature)

Gauss's Law (Angle, Area, Charge, Dielectric Constant, Electric Flux, Length, Magnetic Flux. Permeability)

Kerr Magneto-Optic Effect (Angle, Chemical Composition, Color, Light, Magnetic Flux, Polarization, Reflection)

Luminescence (Absorption, Chemical Composition, Color, Emissivity, Energy (K.E.), Intensity, Light, Magnetic Flux, Radiation, Temperature)

Magnetic Behavior of Materials (Chemical Composition, Magnetic Flux)

Magnetic Dispersion of Sound (Current, Density, Frequency, Magnetic Flux, Permeability, Resistivity, Sound, Transmission (Speed of Sound))

Magnetic Effects (Current, Direction, Intensity, Length, Light, Magnetic Flux, Permeability, Resistivity)

Magnetic Susceptance (Magnetic Flux, Resistivity, Temperature)

Magnetostriction and Allied Effects (Amplitude, Angle, Coefficient of Expansion, Current, Force, Frequency, Length, Magnetic Flux, Permeability, Sound, Stress, Temperature)

Photomagnetic Effect (Light, Magnetic Flux, Potential, Radiation)

Pinch Effect (Area, Current, Force, Magnetic Flux, Pressure)

Residual Voltage (Charge, Current, Magnetic Flux, Potential, Time)

Wood and Ellett Effect (Frequency, Light, Magnetic Flux, Polarization, Radiation, Vapor Pressure)

Zeeman Effect (Color, Frequency, Light, Magnetic Flux, Polarization)

MAGNIFICATION

Snell's Law (Angle, Density, Frequency, Index of Refraction, Light, Magnification, Molecular Weight, Speed of Light, Temperature)

MASS

Archimedes' Principle (Density, Mass, Specific Gravity, Volume)

Conservation Laws (Charge, Energy (K.E.), Energy (P.E.), Light, Mass, Momentum, Sound, Velocity)

Coulomb's Law (Charge, Dielectric Constant, Force, Length, Magnetic Flux, Mass, Permeability)

Eotvos Effect (Direction, Mass, Position, Velocity)

Faraday's Law of Electrolysis (Chemical Composition, Concentration, Current, Energy (P.E.), Mass, Molecular Weight, Potential, Resistivity)

Fluid Flow Effects (Density, Energy (K.E.), Flow, Length, Mass, Pressure, Specific Gravity, Temperature, Transmission, (Speed of Sound), Vapor Pressure, Velocity, Viscosity)

Group Displacement Law (Charge, Chemical Composition, Emissivity, Energy (P.E.), Mass, Radiation, Time)

Henry's Law (Chemical Composition, Gas, Liquid, Mass, Pressure, Temperature, Volume)

Ideal Gas Laws (Gas, Mass, Pressure, Temperature, Volume)

Newton's Law of Heating and Cooling (Area, Conductivity, Film Coefficient, Heat Flux, Mass, Specific Heat, Temperature, Volume)

Newton's Laws (Acceleration, Direction, Force, Mass, Velocity)

Schrodinger's Wave Equation (Energy (P.E.), Frequency, Mass, Propagation, Time, Velocity)

MATTER—*see* **CHEMICAL COMPOSITION**

MOLECULAR WEIGHT

Faraday's Law of Electrolysis (Chemical Composition, Concentration, Current, Energy (P.E.), Mass, Molecular Weight, Potential Resistivity)

Raoult's Law (Concentration, Gas, Liquid, Molecular Weight, Solid, Temperature, Vapor Pressure)

Snell's Law (Angle, Density, Frequency, Index of Refraction, Light, Magnification, Molecular Weight, Speed of Light, Temperature)

MOMENTUM

Conservation Laws (Charge, Energy (K.E.), Energy (P.E.), Light, Mass, Momentum, Sound, Velocity)

MOTION—*see* VELOCITY

NOISE—*see* SOUND

OPAQUENESS

Christiansen Effect (Color, Frequency, Light, Opaqueness, Temperature, Translucence)

Kerr Effect (Electrostatic) (Angle, Chemical Composition, Electric Flux, Frequency, Light, Opaqueness, Polarization, Time, Translucence)

Liquid Crystal Phase (Chemical Composition, Diffraction, Light, Liquid, Opaqueness, Temperature, Translucence)

OPTICS—*see* Cross Reference by Fields of Science

PERMEABILITY

Barkhausen Effect (Inductance, Magnetic Flux, Permeability, Sound)

Coulomb's Law (Charge, Dielectric Constant, Force, Length, Magnetic Flux, Mass, Permeability)

Curie-Weiss Law (Chemical Composition, Magnetic Flux, Permeability, Temperature)

Gauss's Law (Angle, Area, Charge, Dielectric Constant, Electric Flux, Length, Magnetic Flux, Permeability)

Magnetic Dispersion of Sound (Current, Density, Frequency, Magnetic Flux, Permeability, Resistivity, Sound, Transmission (Speed of Sound))

Magnetic Effects (Current, Direction, Intensity, Length, Light, Magnetic Flux, Permeability, Resistivity)

Magnetostriction and Allied Effects (Amplitude, Angle, Coefficient of Expansion, Current, Force, Frequency, Length, Magnetic Flux, Permeability, Sound, Stress, Temperature)

Skin Effect (Current, Frequency, Inductance, Length, Permeability, Resistivity, Temperature)

PITCH—*see* FREQUENCY

POLARIZATION

Brewster's Law (Angle, Index of Refraction, Polarization)

Faraday Effect (Angle, Chemical Composition, Frequency, Index of Refraction, Length, Light, Magnetic Flux, Polarization, Temperature)

Ferroelectric Phenomena (Capacitance, Charge, Dielectric Constant, Electric Flux, Polarization, Potential, Temperature)

Kerr Effect (Electrostatic) (Angle, Chemical Composition, Electric Flux, Frequency, Light, Opaqueness, Polarization, Time, Translucence)

Kerr Magneto-Optic Effect (Angle, Chemical Composition, Color, Light, Magnetic Flux, Polarization, Reflection)

Optical Rotary Power (Angle, Chemical Composition, Concentration, Frequency, Length, Light, Polarization)

Photoelectric Effect (Chemical Composition, Energy (K.E.), Frequency, Intensity, Light, Polarization, Potential, Speed of Light)

Stress and Strain Effects (Chemical Composition, Force, Frequency, Length, Light, Polarization, Strain, Stress, Temperature, Time, Volume, Yield Point)

Wood and Ellett Effect (Frequency, Light, Magnetic Flux, Polarization, Radiation, Vapor Pressure)

Zeeman Effect (Color, Frequency, Light, Magnetic Flux, Polarization)

POSITION

Cosmic Rays (Angle, Concentration, Direction, Energy (K.E.), Position, Radiation)

Eotvos Effect (Direction, Mass, Position, Velocity)

POTENTIAL

Ampère's Law (Angle, Charge, Current, Force, Length, Magnetic Flux, Potential, Velocity)

Bremstrahlung Radiation (Acceleration, Density, Electric Flux, Energy (K.E.), Frequency, Potential, Radiation)

Capacitance/Dielectric (Capacitance, Charge, Dielectric Constant, Length, Potential, Temperature)

Electrocapillarity (Current, Flow, Force, Potential, Pressure, Surface Tension)

Electrokinetic Phenomena (Chemical Composition, Current, Direction, Flow, Potential, Pressure)

Faraday's Law of Electrolysis (Chemical Composition, Concentration, Current, Energy (P.E.), Mass, Molecular Weight, Potential, Resistivity)

Faraday's Law of Inductance (Current, Energy (P.E.), Inductance, Length, Magnetic Flux, Potential, Time, Velocity)

Ferranti Effect (Capacitance, Frequency, Inductance, Length, Potential, Resistivity)

Ferroelectric Phenomena (Capacitance, Charge, Dielectric Constant, Electric Flux, Polarization, Potential, Temperature)

Fick's Laws (Area, Chemical Composition, Concentration, Liquid, Potential, Temperature, Time)

Johnsen-Rahbek and/or Winslow Effect (Chemical Composition, Electric Flux, Friction, Liquid, Potential)

Joule's Law (Current, Energy (K.E.), Heat Flux, Potential, Power, Resistivity, Time)

Kirchhoff's Laws (Current, Potential)

Ohm's Law (Capacitance, Current, Frequency, Inductance, Potential, Resistivity)

Paschen's Law (Chemical Composition, Gas, Length, Potential, Pressure)

Photoelectric Effect (Chemical Composition, Energy (K.E.), Frequency, Intensity, Light, Polarization, Potential, Speed of Light)

Photomagnetic Effect (Light, Magnetic Flux, Potential, Radiation)

Piezoelectric Effect (Charge, Force, Frequency, Potential, Strain)

Pyroelectric Effect (Charge, Potential, Temperature)

Residual Voltage (Charge, Current, Magnetic Flux, Potential, Time)
Shot Effect (Current, Emissivity, Potential, Sound, Temperature)
Thermoelastic Effect (Force, Potential, Strain, Stress, Temperature)
Thermoelectric Effects (Chemical Composition, Conductivity, Current, Direction, Force, Heat Flux, Potential, Temperature)
Triboelectricity (Charge, Chemical Composition, Friction, Potential, Velocity)
Volta Effect (Charge, Chemical Composition, Potential, Temperature)
Wien Effect (Concentration, Current, Liquid, Potential, Resistivity)
Zener Effect (Area, Chemical Composition, Current, Light, Potential, Resistivity, Temperature)

POWER

Joule's Law (Current, Energy (K.E.), Heat Flux, Potential, Power, Resistivity, Time)
Thermodynamic Laws (Energy (K.E.), Energy (P.E.), Entropy, Enthalpy, Heat Flux, Power, Pressure, Temperature)
Weber-Fechner Law (Energy (K.E.), Force, Length, Light, Power, Sound, Temperature)

PRESSURE

Bernoulli's Theorem (Density, Energy (K.E.), Energy (P.E.), Flow, Pressure Velocity)
Cavitation (Energy (K.E.), Pressure, Sound, Temperature, Vapor Pressure, Velocity)
Electrocapillarity (Current, Flow, Force, Potential, Pressure, Surface Tension)
Electrokinetic Phenomena (Chemical Composition, Current, Direction, Flow, Potential, Pressure)
Fluid Flow Effects (Density, Energy (K.E.), Flow, Length, Mass, Pressure, Specific Gravity, Temperature, Transmission (Speed of Sound), Vapor Pressure, Velocity, Viscosity)
Gibbs Theory of Equilibria (Concentration, Pressure, Temperature)
Graham's Law (Chemical Composition, Concentration, Flow, Gas, Liquid, Pressure, Temperature, Time)
Henry's Law (Chemical Composition, Gas, Liquid, Mass, Pressure, Temperature, Volume)
Ideal Gas Laws (Gas, Mass, Pressure, Temperature, Volume)
Joule-Thomson Effect (Energy (K.E.), Enthalpy, Gas, Heat Flux, Pressure, Temperature, Volume)
Le Châtelier's Law (Concentration, Pressure, Stress, Temperature, Volume)
Paschen's Law (Chemical Composition, Gas, Length, Potential, Pressure)
Pinch Effect (Area, Current, Force, Magnetic Flux, Pressure)
Radiation Pressure (Light, Pressure, Radiation, Speed of Light)
Resistance/Pressure Effect (Chemical Composition, Pressure, Resistivity)
State and Change of State (Boiling Point, Chemical Composition, Enthalpy, Freezing Point, Gas, Liquid, Pressure, Solid, Temperature)
Surface Tension (Concentration, Force, Length, Liquid, Pressure, Surface Tension, Temperature)
Thermodynamic Laws (Energy (K.E.), Energy (P.E.), Enthalpy, Entropy, Heat Flux, Power, Pressure, Temperature)

PROPAGATION

Schrodinger's Wave Equation (Energy (P.E.), Frequency, Mass, Propagation, Time, Velocity)

Total Reflection (Angle, Density, Direction, Index of Refraction, Light, Propagation, Reflection, Speed of Light)

RADIATION

Bremstrahlung Radiation (Acceleration, Density, Electric Flux, Energy (K.E.), Frequency, Potential, Radiation)

Compton Effect (Absorption, Dispersion, Frequency, Radiation)

Cosmic Rays (Angle, Concentration, Direction, Energy (K.E.), Position, Radiation)

Diffraction (Angle, Color, Diffraction, Frequency, Length, Light, Radiation, Sound)

Doppler-Fizeau Effect (Frequency, Light, Radiation, Reflection, Sound, Velocity)

Fission (Emissivity, Energy (K.E.), Energy (P.E.), Radiation)

Geiger-Nuttal Rule (Chemical Composition, Energy (K.E.), Length, Radiation, Time, Velocity)

Group Displacement Law (Charge, Chemical Composition, Emissivity, Energy (P.E.), Mass, Radiation, Time)

Hertz Effect (Charge, Current, Light, Radiation)

Interference (Frequency, Length, Light, Radiation, Sound)

Lambert's Law (Absorption, Chemical Composition, Frequency, Length, Light, Liquid, Radiation)

Luminescence (Absorption, Chemical Composition, Color, Emissivity, Energy (K.E.), Intensity, Light, Magnetic Flux, Radiation, Temperature)

Periodic Law (Chemical Composition, Radiation)

Photomagnetic Effect (Light, Magnetic Flux, Potential, Radiation)

Quantum Theory (Energy (K.E.), Frequency, Radiation, Speed of Light, Temperature)

Radiation Pressure (Light, Pressure, Radiation, Speed of Light)

Radioactivity (Charge, Emissivity, Energy (K.E.), Radiation)

Stefan-Boltzmann Law (Absorption, Emissivity, Frequency, Light, Radiation, Temperature)

Wien's Displacement Law (Emissivity, Frequency, Intensity, Light, Radiation, Temperature)

Wood and Ellett Effect (Frequency, Light, Magnetic Flux, Polarization, Radiation, Vapor Pressure)

Zener Effect (Area, Chemical Composition, Current, Light, Potential, Radiation, Resistivity, Temperature)

REFLECTION

Doppler-Fizeau Effect (Frequency, Light, Radiation, Sound, Reflection, Velocity)

Kerr Magneto-Optic Effect (Angle, Chemical Composition, Color, Light, Magnetic Flux, Polarization, Reflection)

Total Reflection (Angle, Density, Direction, Index of Refraction, Light, Propagation, Reflection, Speed of Light)

RESISTIVITY

Debye Frequency Effect (Chemical Composition, Concentration, Current, Frequency, Resistivity)

Faraday's Law of Electrolysis (Chemical Composition, Concentration, Current, Energy (P.E.), Mass, Molecular Weight, Potential, Resistivity)

Ferranti Effect (Capacitance, Frequency, Inductance, Length, Potential, Resistivity)

Joule's Law (Current, Energy (K.E.), Heat Flux, Potential, Power, Resistivity, Time)

Kohlrausch's Law (Chemical Composition, Concentration, Current, Dielectric Constant, Resistivity, Temperature)

Magnetic Dispersion of Sound (Current, Density, Frequency, Magnetic Flux, Permeability, Resistivity, Sound, Transmission (Speed of Sound))

Magnetic Effects (Current, Direction, Intensity, Length, Light, Magnetic Flux, Permeability, Resistivity)

Magnetic Susceptance (Magnetic Flux, Resistivity, Temperature)

Ohm's Law (Capacitance, Current, Frequency, Inductance, Potential, Resistivity)

Proximity Effect (Current, Frequency, Length, Resistivity)

Resistance/Dimension (Length, Resistivity, Strain)

Resistance/Pressure Effect (Chemical Composition, Pressure, Resistivity)

Resistance/Temperature (Chemical Composition, Resistivity, Temperature)

Skin Effect (Current, Frequency, Inductance, Length, Permeability, Resistivity, Temperature)

Wiedemann-Franz's Law (Chemical Composition, Resistivity, Solid, Temperature)

Wien Effect (Concentration, Current, Liquid, Potential, Resistivity)

Zener Effect (Area, Chemical Composition, Current, Light, Potential, Radiation, Resistivity, Temperature)

RESOLVING POWER—*see* **MAGNIFICATION**

RESONANCE

Organ Pipe Resonance (Frequency, Gas, Length, Resonance, Sound)

SOLID

Raoult's Law (Concentration, Gas, Liquid, Molecular Weight, Solid, Temperature, Vapor Pressure)

State and Change of State (Boiling Point, Chemical Composition, Enthalpy, Freezing Point, Gas, Liquid, Pressure, Solid, Temperature)

Wiedemann-Franz's Law (Chemical Composition, Resistivity, Solid, Temperature)

SOUND

Barkhausen Effect (Inductance, Magnetic Flux, Permeability, Sound)

Cavitation (Energy (K.E.), Pressure, Sound, Temperature, Vapor Pressure, Velocity)

Conservation Laws (Charge, Energy (K.E.), Energy (P.E.), Light, Mass, Momentum, Sound, Velocity)

Diffraction (Angle, Color, Diffraction, Frequency, Length, Light, Radiation, Sound)

Doppler-Fizeau Effect (Frequency, Light, Radiation, Reflection, Sound, Velocity)

Interference (Frequency, Length, Light, Radiation, Sound)

Magnetic Dispersion of Sound (Current, Density, Frequency, Magnetic Flux, Permeability, Resistivity, Sound, Transmission (Speed of Sound))

Magnetostriction and Allied Effects (Amplitude, Angle, Coefficient of Expansion,

Current, Force, Frequency, Length, Magnetic Flux, Permeability, Sound, Stress, Temperature)
Organ Pipe Resonance (Frequency, Gas, Length, Resonance, Sound)
Shot Effect (Current, Emissivity, Potential, Sound, Temperature)
Weber-Fechner Law (Energy (K.E.), Force, Length, Light, Power, Sound, Temperature)

SPECIFIC GRAVITY

Archimedes' Principle (Density, Mass, Specific Gravity, Volume)
Fluid Flow Effects (Density, Energy (K.E.), Flow, Length, Mass, Pressure, Specific Gravity, Temperature, Transmission (Speed of Sound), Vapor Pressure, Velocity, Viscosity)

SPECIFIC HEAT

Constant Heat Capacity Law (Chemical Composition, Specific Heat, Temperature)
Newton's Law of Heating and Cooling (Area, Conductivity, Film Coefficient, Heat Flux, Mass, Specific Heat, Temperature, Volume)

SPEED OF LIGHT

Photoelectric Effect (Chemical Composition, Energy (K.E.), Frequency, Intensity, Light, Polarization, Potential, Speed of Light)
Quantum Theory (Energy (K.E.), Frequency, Radiation, Speed of Light, Temperature)
Radiation Pressure (Light, Pressure, Radiation, Speed of Light)
Snell's Law (Angle, Density, Frequency, Index of Refraction, Light, Magnification, Molecular Weight, Speed of Light, Temperature)
Total Reflection (Angle, Density, Direction, Index of Refraction, Light, Propagation, Reflection, Speed of Light)

STATICS—*see* POSITION

STRAIN

Bauschinger Effect (Force, Length, Strain, Stress, Temperature, Yield Point)
Elastic Limit (Chemical Composition, Strain, Stress)
Friction Effects (Force, Friction, Strain, Stress, Velocity, Viscosity)
Gladstone and Dale's Law (Angle, Chemical Composition, Color, Density, Index of Refraction, Strain, Temperature)
Hooke's Law (Area, Force, Length, Strain, Stress)
Memory Metals (Force, Heat Flux, Length, Strain, Stress, Temperature)
Piezoelectric Effect (Charge, Force, Frequency, Potential, Strain)
Poisson's Coefficient (Force, Length, Strain, Volume)
Resistance/Dimension (Length, Resistivity, Strain)
Stress and Strain Effects (Chemical Composition, Force, Frequency, Length, Light, Polarization, Strain, Stress, Temperature, Time, Volume, Yield Point)
Thermoelastic Effect (Force, Potential, Strain, Stress, Temperature)

STRESS

Bauschinger Effect (Force, Length, Strain, Stress, Temperature, Yield Point)
Elastic Limit (Chemical Composition, Strain, Stress)

Friction Effects (Force, Friction, Strain, Stress, Velocity, Viscosity)

Hooke's Law (Area, Force, Length, Strain, Stress)

Le Châtelier's Law (Concentration, Pressure, Stress, Temperature, Volume)

Magnetostriction and Allied Effects (Amplitude, Angle, Coefficient of Expansion, Current, Force, Frequency, Length, Magnetic Flux, Permeability, Sound, Stress, Temperature)

Memory Metals (Force, Heat Flux, Length, Strain, Stress, Temperature)

Stress and Strain Effects (Chemical Composition, Force, Frequency, Length, Light, Polarization, Strain, Stress, Temperature, Time, Volume, Yield Point)

Thermoelastic Effect (Force, Potential, Strain, Stress, Temperature)

SURFACE TENSION

Adsorption (Chemical Composition, Concentration, Gas, Surface Tension)

Electrocapillarity (Current, Flow, Force, Potential, Pressure, Surface Tension)

Kelvin's Principle for Fluid Drops (Density, Length, Liquid, Surface Tension, Temperature, Vapor Pressure)

Surface Tension (Concentration, Force, Length, Liquid, Pressure, Surface Tension, Temperature)

TEMPERATURE

Bauschinger Effect (Force, Length, Strain, Stress, Temperature, Yield Point)

Biot and Fourier's Law (Area, Heat Flux, Temperature, Time)

Brownian Movement (Temperature, Velocity)

Capacitance/Dielectric (Capacitance, Charge, Dielectric Constant, Length, Potential, Temperature)

Cavitation (Energy (K.E.), Pressure, Sound, Temperature, Vapor Pressure, Velocity)

Christiansen Effect (Color, Frequency, Light, Opaqueness, Temperature, Translucence)

Constant Heat Capacity Law (Chemical Composition, Specific Heat, Temperature)

Curie-Weiss Law (Chemical Composition, Magnetic Flux, Permeability, Temperature)

Expansion, Temperature (Coefficient of Expansion, Length, Temperature, Volume)

Faraday Effect (Angle, Chemical Composition, Frequency, Index of Refraction, Length, Light, Magnetic Flux, Polarization, Temperature)

Ferroelectric Phenomena (Capacitance, Charge, Dielectric Constant, Electric Flux, Polarization, Potential, Temperature)

Fick's Laws (Area, Chemical Composition, Concentration, Liquid, Potential, Temperature, Time)

Fluid Flow Effects (Density, Energy (K.E.), Flow, Length, Mass, Pressure, Specific Gravity, Temperature, Transmission (Speed of Sound), Vapor Pressure, Velocity, Viscosity)

Galvanomagnetic and Thermomagnetic Effects (Angle, Chemical Composition, Current, Heat Flux, Magnetic Flux, Temperature)

Gibbs Theory of Equilibria (Concentration, Pressure, Temperature)

Gladstone and Dale's Law (Angle, Chemical Composition, Color, Density, Index of Refraction, Strain, Temperature)

Graham's Law (Chemical Composition, Concentration, Flow, Gas, Liquid, Pressure, Temperature, Time)

Henry's Law (Chemical Composition, Gas, Liquid, Mass, Pressure, Temperature, Volume)

Ideal Gas Laws (Gas, Mass, Pressure, Temperature, Volume)

Joule-Thomson Effect (Energy (K.E.), Enthalpy, Gas, Heat Flux, Pressure, Temperature, Volume)

Kelvin's Principle for Fluid Drops (Density, Length, Liquid, Surface Tension, Temperature, Vapor Pressure)

Kohlrausch's Law (Chemical Composition, Concentration, Current, Dielectric Constant, Resistivity, Temperature)

Le Châtelier's Law (Concentration, Pressure, Stress, Temperature, Volume)

Leidenfrost's Phenomena (Boiling Point, Heat Flux, Liquid, Temperature)

Liquid Crystal Phase (Chemical Composition, Diffraction, Light, Liquid, Opaqueness, Temperature, Translucence)

Luminescence (Absorption, Chemical Composition, Color, Emissivity, Energy (K.E.), Intensity, Light, Magnetic Flux, Radiation, Temperature)

Magnetic Susceptance (Magnetic Flux, Resistivity, Temperature)

Magnetostriction and Allied Effects (Amplitude, Angle, Coefficient of Expansion, Current, Force, Frequency, Length, Magnetic Flux, Permeability, Sound, Stress, Temperature)

Memory Metals (Force, Heat Flux, Length, Strain, Stress, Temperature)

Newton's Law of Heating and Cooling (Area, Conductivity, Film Coefficient, Heat Flux, Mass, Specific Heat, Temperature, Volume)

Pyroelectric Effect (Charge Potential, Temperature)

Quantum Theory (Energy (K.E.), Frequency, Radiation, Speed of Light, Temperature)

Raoult's Law (Concentration, Gas, Liquid, Molecular Weight, Solid, Temperature, Vapor Pressure)

Resistance/Temperature (Chemical Composition, Resistivity, Temperature)

Richardson's Effect (Chemical Composition, Current, Emissivity, Temperature)

Shot Effect (Current, Emissivity, Potential, Sound, Temperature)

Skin Effect (Current, Frequency, Inductance, Length, Permeability, Resistivity, Temperature)

Snell's Law (Angle, Density, Frequency, Index of Refraction, Light, Magnification, Molecular Weight, Speed of Light, Temperature)

State and Change of State (Boiling Point, Chemical Composition, Enthalpy, Freezing Point, Gas, Liquid, Pressure, Solid, Temperature)

Stefan-Boltzmann Law (Absorption, Emissivity, Frequency, Light, Radiation, Temperature)

Stokes's Law (Density, Gas, Length, Temperature, Velocity, Viscosity)

Stress and Strain Effects (Chemical Composition, Force, Frequency, Length, Light, Polarization, Strain, Stress, Temperature, Time, Volume, Yield Point)

Surface Tension (Concentration, Force, Length, Liquid, Pressure, Surface Tension, Temperature)

Thermodynamic Laws (Energy (K.E.), Energy (P.E.), Enthalpy, Entropy, Heat Flux, Power, Pressure, Temperature)

Thermoelastic Effect (Force, Potential, Strain, Stress, Temperature)

Thermoelectric Effects (Chemical Composition, Conductivity, Current, Direction, Force, Heat Flux, Potential, Temperature)

Volta Effect (Charge, Chemical Composition, Potential, Temperature)

Weber-Fechner Law (Energy (K.E.), Force, Length, Light, Power, Sound, Temperature)

Wiedemann-Franz's Law (Chemical Composition, Resistivity, Solid, Temperature)

Wien's Displacement Law (Emissivity, Frequency, Intensity, Light, Radiation, Temperature)

Zener Effect (Area, Chemical Composition, Current, Light, Potential, Resistivity, Temperature)

THERMAL CONDUCTIVITY—*see* CONDUCTIVITY

TIME

Biot and Fourier's Law (Area, Heat Flux, Temperature, Time)

Faraday's Law of Inductance (Current, Energy (P.E.), Inductance, Length, Magnetic Flux, Potential, Time, Velocity)

Fick's Laws (Area, Chemical Composition, Concentration, Liquid, Potential, Temperature, Time)

Geiger-Nuttal Rule (Chemical Composition, Energy (K.E.), Length, Radiation, Time, Velocity)

Graham's Law (Chemical Composition, Concentration, Flow, Gas, Liquid, Pressure, Temperature, Time)

Group Displacement Law (Charge, Chemical Composition, Emissivity, Energy (P.E.), Mass, Radiation, Time)

Joule's Law (Current, Energy (K.E.), Heat Flux, Potential, Power, Resistivity, Time)

Kepler's Laws (Acceleration, Area, Force, Length, Time)

Kerr Effect (Electrostatic) (Angle, Chemical Composition, Electric Flux, Frequency, Light, Opaqueness, Polarization, Time, Translucence)

Residual Voltage (Charge, Current, Magnetic Flux, Potential, Time)

Schrodinger's Wave Equation (Energy (P.E.), Frequency, Mass, Propagation, Time, Velocity)

Stress and Strain Effects (Chemical Composition, Force, Frequency, Length, Light, Polarization, Strain, Stress, Temperature, Time, Volume, Yield Point)

TRANSLUCENCE

Christiansen Effect (Color, Frequency, Light, Opaqueness, Temperature, Translucence)

Kerr Effect (Electrostatic) (Angle, Chemical Composition, Electric Flux, Frequency, Light, Opaqueness, Polarization, Time, Translucence)

Liquid Crystal Phase (Chemical Composition, Diffraction, Light, Liquid, Opaqueness, Temperature, Translucence)

TRANSMISSION (SPEED OF SOUND)

Fluid Flow Effects (Density, Energy (K.E.), Flow, Length, Mass, Pressure, Specific Gravity, Temperature, Transmission (Speed of Sound), Vapor Pressure, Velocity, Viscosity)

Magnetic Dispersion of Sound (Current, Density, Frequency, Magnetic Flux, Permeability, Resistivity, Sound, Transmission (Speed of Sound))

VAPOR PRESSURE

Cavitation (Energy (K.E.), Pressure, Sound, Temperature, Vapor Pressure, Velocity)

Fluid Flow Effects (Density, Energy (K.E.), Flow, Length, Mass, Pressure, Specific Gravity, Temperature, Transmission (Speed of Sound), Vapor Pressure, Velocity, Viscosity)

Kelvin's Principle for Fluid Drops (Density, Length, Liquid, Surface Tension, Temperature, Vapor Pressure)

Raoult's Law (Concentration, Gas, Liquid, Molecular Weight, Solid, Temperature, Vapor Pressure)

Wood and Ellett Effect (Frequency, Light, Magnetic Flux, Polarization, Radiation, Vapor Pressure)

VELOCITY

Ampère's Law (Angle, Charge, Current, Force, Length, Magnetic Flux, Potential, Velocity)

Bernoulli's Theorem (Density, Energy (K.E.), Energy (P.E.), Flow, Pressure, Velocity)

Brownian Movement (Temperature, Velocity)

Cavitation (Energy (K.E.), Pressure, Sound, Temperature, Vapor Pressure, Velocity)

Conservation Laws (Charge, Energy (K.E.), Energy (P.E.), Light, Mass, Momentum, Sound, Velocity)

Doppler-Fizeau Effect (Frequency, Light, Radiation, Reflection, Sound, Velocity)

Eotvos Effect (Direction, Mass, Position, Velocity)

Faraday's Law of Induction (Current, Energy (P.E.), Inductance, Length, Magnetic Flux, Potential, Time, Velocity)

Fluid Flow Effects (Density, Energy (K.E.), Flow, Length, Mass, Pressure, Specific Gravity, Temperature, Transmission (Speed of Sound), Vapor Pressure, Velocity, Viscosity)

Friction Effects (Force, Friction, Strain, Stress, Velocity, Viscosity)

Geiger-Nuttal Rule (Chemical Composition, Energy (K.E.), Length, Radiation, Time, Velocity)

Newton's Laws (Acceleration, Direction, Force, Mass, Velocity)

Schrodinger's Wave Equation (Energy (P.E.), Frequency, Mass, Propagation, Time, Velocity)

Stokes's Law (Density, Gas, Length, Temperature, Velocity, Viscosity)

Triboelectricity (Charge, Chemical Composition, Friction, Potential, Velocity)

VISCOSITY

Fluid Flow Effects (Density, Energy (K.E.), Flow, Length, Mass, Pressure, Specific Gravity, Temperature, Transmission, (Speed of Sound) Vapor Pressure, Velocity, Viscosity)

Friction Effects (Force, Friction, Strain, Stress, Velocity, Viscosity)

Stokes's Law (Density, Gas, Length, Temperature, Velocity, Viscosity)

VOLTAGE—*see* **POTENTIAL**

VOLUME

Archimedes' Principle (Density, Mass, Specific Gravity, Volume)

Expansion/Temperature (Coefficient of Expansion, Length, Temperature, Volume)

Henry's Law (Chemical Composition, Gas, Liquid, Mass, Pressure, Temperature, Volume)

Ideal Gas Laws (Gas, Mass, Pressure, Temperature, Volume)

Joule-Thomson Effect (Energy (K.E.), Enthalpy, Gas, Heat Flux, Pressure, Temperature, Volume)

Le Châtelier's Law (Concentration, Pressure, Stress, Temperature, Volume)

Newton's Law of Heating and Cooling (Area, Conductivity, Film Coefficient, Heat Flux, Mass, Specific Heat, Temperature, Volume)

Poisson's Coefficient (Force, Length, Strain, Volume)

Stress and Strain Effects (Chemical Composition, Force, Frequency, Length, Light, Polarization, Strain, Stress, Temperature, Time, Volume, Yield Point)

WAVE LENGTH—*see* **FREQUENCY**

WEIGHT—*see* **MASS**

WORK—*see* **ENERGY**

YIELD POINT

Bauschinger Effect (Force, Length, Strain, Stress, Temperature, Yield Point)

Stress and Strain Effects (Chemical Composition, Force, Frequency, Length, Light, Polarization, Strain, Stress, Temperature, Time, Volume, Yield Point)

Cross References by Fields
of Science

ACOUSTICS

Cavitation
Diffraction
Doppler-Fizeau Effect
Interference
Luminescence
Magnetic Dispersion of Sound
Organ Pipe Resonance
Weber-Fechner Law

ATOMIC PHYSICS

Absorption
Boltzmann Distribution Law
Bremstrahlung Radiation
Compton Effect
Conservation Laws
Constant Heat Capacity Law
Cosmic Rays
Diffraction
Fission
Geiger-Nutall Rule
Group Displacement Law
Hertz Effect
Luminescence
Photoelectric Effects

Quantum Theory
Radiation Pressure
Radioactivity
Richardson's Effect (Edison Effect)
Schrodinger's Wave Equation
Stark Effect
Stefan-Boltzmann Law (Kirchhoff's Law)
Stokes's Law of Fluorescence
Wiedemann-Franz's Law
Wien's Displacement Law
Wood and Ellett Effect, or Resonance
    Radiation
Zeeman Effect

CHEMISTRY (AND PHYSICAL CHEMISTRY)

Absorption
Adsorption
Arrhenius Theory of Electrolytic
    Dissociation
Brownian Movement
Conservation Laws
Debye Frequency Effect
Electrocapillarity
Electrokinetic Phenomena

264

Faraday's Law of Electrolysis
Fick's Law
Gibbs Theory of Equilibria
Graham's Law
Henry's Law
Ideal Gas Laws
Joule-Thomson Effect
Kohlrausch's Law
Le Châtelier's Law
Liquid Crystal Effect
Luminescence
Periodic Law (or Table)
Raoult's Law
Snell's Law, The Law of Refraction
State and Change of State
Stress Strain Effects
Surface Tension
Volta Effect
Wien Effect

ELECTRICITY AND MAGNETISM

Ampère's Law
Ampère's (Biot-Savart) Law
Barkhausen Effect
Capacitance/Dielectric
Conservation Laws
Corbino Effect
Coulomb's Law
Curie-Weiss Law
Debye Frequency Effect
Electrocapillarity
Electrokinetic Phenomena
Faraday Effect (Magneto-optical Rotation)
Faraday's Law of Electrolysis
Faraday's Law of Induction
Ferranti Effect
Ferroelectric Phenomena
Galvanomagnetic and Thermomagnetic Effects
Gauss's Law
Hertz Effect
Impedance/Frequency
Johnson-Rahbeck and/or Winslow Effect
Joule's Law
Kerr Effect (Electrostatic)
Kerr Magneto-optic Effect
Kirchhoff's Laws
Kohlrausch's Law

Lichtenecker's Law
Luminescence
Magnetic Behavior of Materials
Magnetic Dispersion of Sound
Magnetic Effects
Magnetic Susceptance (Gauss Effect)
Magnetostriction and Allied Effects
Paschen's Law
Photoelectric Effects
Photomagnetic Effect
Piezoelectric Effect
Pinch Effect
Proximity Effect
Pyroelectric Effect
Residual Voltage
Resistance/Dimension
Resistance/Pressure Effect
Resistance/Temperature
Richardson's Effect (Edison Effect)
Schrodinger's Wave Equation
Shot Effect
Skin Effect
Thermoelastic Effect
Thermoelectric Effects
Thomson and Benedick Effects
Triboelectricity
Volta Effect
Wiedemann-Franz's Law
Wien Effect
Wood and Ellett Effect or Resonance Radiation
Zeeman Effect
Zener Effect

FLUID MECHANICS

Archimedes' Principle
Bernoulli's Theorem
Cavitation
Electrocapillarity
Electrokinetic Phenomena
Fluid Flow Effects
Friction Effects
Graham's Law
Henry's Law
Ideal Gas Laws
Joule-Thomson Effect
Kelvin's Principle for Fluid Drops
Liquid Crystal Phase
Resistance/Pressure Effect

Stokes's Law
Surface Tension

GENERAL PHYSICS

Adsorption
Ampère's Law
Ampère's (Biot-Savart) Law
Archimedes' Principle
Bauschinger Effect
Bernoulli's Theorem
Biot and Fourier's Law
Brownian Movement
Capacitance/Dielectric
Conservation Laws
Constant Heat Capacity Law
Coulomb's Law
Doppler-Fizeau Effect
Electrocapillarity
Eotvos Effect
Expansion/Temperature or Thermal Expansion
Faraday's Law of Induction
Fick's Law
Fluid Flow Effect
Friction Effects
Gauss's Law
Hooke's Law
Ideal Gas Laws
Joule's Law
Joule-Thomson Effect
Kelvin's Principle for Fluid Drops
Kepler's Laws
Lambert's Law, Absorption Coefficient
Le Châtelier's Law
Leidenfrosts' Phenomena
Liquid Crystal Phase
Luminescence
Magnetic Effects
Memory Metals
Newton's Laws
Newton's Law of Heating and Cooling
Ohm's Law
Periodic Law (or Table)
Resistance/Dimension
Resistance/Temperature
Schrodinger's Wave Equation
Snell's Law, The Law of Refraction
State and Change of State
Stokes's Law

Stress-Strain Effects
Thermodynamics Laws

MECHANICS

Bauschinger Effect
Coulomb's Law
Elastic Limit
Friction Effects
Hooke's Law
Johnson-Rahbek and/or Winslow Effect
Magnetic Dispersion of Sound
Newton's Laws
Piezoelectric Effect
Poisson's Coefficient (or ratio)
Resistance/Dimension
Thermoelectric Effects
Triboelectricity

OPTICS

Absorption
Brewster's Law
Christiansen Effect
Diffraction
Doppler-Fizeau Effect
Faraday Effect (Magneto-optical Rotation)
Gladstone and Dale's Law
Hertz Effect
Interference
Kerr Effect (Electrostatic)
Kerr Magneto-optic Effect
Lambert's Law, Absorption Coefficient
Liquid Crystal Phase
Luminescence
Magnetic Effects
Optical Rotary Power
Photoelectric Effects
Purkinje Effect
Radiation Pressure
Snell's Law, The Law of Refraction
Stephen-Boltzmann Law
Stokes's Law of Fluorescence
Weber-Fechner Law
Wien's Displacement Law
Wood and Ellett Effect or Resonance Radiation
Zeeman Effect

PSYCHOLOGY

Purkinje Effect
Weber-Fechner Law

Laws and Effects Addendum

The following addendum presents many potential entries for the *Physical Laws and Effects* that has been called to the attention of the authors. Because there was not time for research on the background and/or accuracy of these items, they were not included in the main text of this edition. They do, however, provide a measure of usefulness to the text, and are added as an addendum to give the reader an additional source of information, without claiming any credit for the rigor of presentation or the accuracy of description.

Abegg's Rule. Every element has both a positive and a negative maximum chemical valency, the sum of which is always eight. This early view has been substantiated in that an atom may either borrow or loan electrons to other atoms to form a stable chemical compound.

Allotropic Forms. Various elements are able to exist in different forms which may vary widely in color, density, chemical behavior, and magnetic properties. The magnetic susceptibilities of a few elements may be listed.

Tin	Gray	-0.35×10^{-6} (susceptibility per gram)
	White	$+0.025$
Carbon	Graphite	-3.5
	Diamond	-0.49
	Lamp black	-0.4
	Gas carbon	-2.0
Water		-0.720 (for comparison)

Auger Effect. Emission of an electron with the ion being left in a normal state, the excess energy appearing as kinetic energy of the ejected electron; occurring when an atom is excited to an electronic state of higher energy than the lowest ionization energy of the normal atom.

Arrhenius Equation. This describes reaction speed as a function of temperature:

$$\frac{d \, (\log_e k)}{dT} = \frac{E}{RT^2}$$

and

$$\log_e k = -\frac{E}{RT} + C$$

where k = specific reaction rate
E = activation energy of reaction
T = absolute temperature
R = gas constant (to suit T units)

Babinet's Principle. If the illumination at some point from an aperture is zero, then any change in this aperture does not affect the illumination at that point.

Barnett Effect. The magnetization of a body due to its rotation.

Becquerel Effect. An emf results if two electrodes in an electrolyte are unequally illuminated.

Bernoulli's Equation. The velocity of liquid flowing through an orifice is given by:

$$v^2 = 2gh \frac{A^2}{A^2 - a^2}$$

where v = velocity of flow in orifice
g = gravitational acceleration
h = liquid head above orifice
A = Surface area of reservoir
a = orifice area

Berthelot Equation. For gases at low pressures, a modification of the perfect gas law is useful:

$$PV = RT \left[1 + \frac{9}{128} \frac{PT_c}{P_c T} \left(1 - 6 \frac{T_c^2}{T^2} \right) \right]$$

where P = pressure of gas
V = volume of gas
R = gas constant
T = temperature (absolute)
T_c = critical temperature of gas
P_c = critical pressure of gas

Berthelot Principle. Of all possible chemical reactions, that one will occur which will liberate the greatest amount of heat.

Bjerrum Theory of Molecular Spectra. The width of the infrared absorption bands of gases is the same as that expected from molecular vibration and rotation.

Bohr's Correspondence Principle. Electron behavior in atoms approaches the predicted classical physic behavior as the orbit quantum number increases.

Bohr's Theory. This theory states that electrons can exist only in certain orbits, hence the discrete nature of spectral lines which can be emitted only when the electron jumps from one orbit to another. If the electron jumps to a lower orbit, energy is radiated; if to a higher, energy is absorbed.

Boyle Temperature. For those temperatures for which the relation

$$\frac{\partial \, (PV)}{\partial \, P} = 0$$

where P = gas pressure
V = gas volume

Boyle's law holds. As the temperature rises, this Boyle Temperature minimum becomes less pronounced and shifts towards zero on the pressure scale.

Brillouin Effect (Debye-Sears Effect). This is the scattering of radiation by liquids where the two scattered lines lie about 0.04 A on each side of the unmodified line.

Brown Effect. If a selenium crystal is illuminated outside of the interelectrode space, the infrared diffusion through the crystal will affect that portion between the electrodes.

Budde Effect. Chlorine or bromine expand on exposure to light because of the photochemically liberated heat.

Cailletet and Mathias Law. The average density of a liquid and its saturated vapor, both at the same temperature, are a linear function of the temperature.

Carnot's Theorem. All machines working reversibly between a heat source and a heat sink have the same efficiency, regardless of working fluid or mode of operation.

Cauchy Dispersion Formula. This formula predicts the refractive index of most materials satisfactorily after three material constants have been determined:

$$N = A + \frac{B}{\lambda^2} + \frac{C}{\lambda^4} + \cdots$$

where N = refractive index at wavelength
             λ = radiation wavelength
   A, B, C = constants, experimentally determined

Cerenkov (Tscherenkov) Effect. This is usually applied to the bluish luminescence induced in liquid water by electrons and gamma rays. The same effect appears in many transparent materials and the emission may be a continuous spectra extending from ultraviolet to the infrared. The intensity varies as the energy of the exciting radiation and the material.

Chadwick-Goldhaber Effect. This is the dissociation of an atomic nucleus due to gamma ray absorption.

Coherer Action. Some semi-conducting films between conducting particles will break down under the action of radio frequency excitation. Once broken down, this insulating film must be mechanically reestablished for the process to be repeated.

Some types of automatic coherers may be listed:

> *Lodge-Muirhead.* A sharpened steel disc rotates slowly just touching a puddle of mercury. An oil film is applied from a separate oil reservoir.
>
> *Italian Navy.* An iron plate separates two globules of mercury which in turn contacts two carbon rods.
>
> *Tantalum-Mercury.* This is a vacuum-sealed device having a small tantalum wire, with its tip inserted in a mercury pool.
>
> *Fessenden Liquid Barreter.* An electrolytic detector consisting of a small platinum electrode dipping into a nitric acid.

A type which must be mechanically restored is:

> *Branly.* A tube full of metal filings or powder. Iron or nickel was usually employed.

Colson-Russell Effect. Dark markings visible on the developed photographic film often carrying the pattern of the backing paper.

Color Centers in Crystals. Color centers are produced in some crystals such as the alkali halide by radiation. This is used in the dark trace Skiatron oscilloscope tube.

Color Mixing. Any color may be obtained from three primary colors, red, green, and blue.

Craft's Rule. This equation gives the change of liquid boiling point for a pressure change.

$$\Delta t = c(273 + t)(760/p)$$

where t = temperature, °C

p = pressure in mm Hg

c = a constant

Crookes Dark Space. As a gas discharge tube is gradually exhausted, the cathode glow leaves the cathode and leaves a dark space at this electrode. This is the Crookes dark space, or the Hittorf dark space. If the pressure is low enough, this dark space fills the entire tube.

Dalton's Law of Gas Solubility. The individual gases in a gaseous mixture, if in equilibrium with a liquid, dissolve independently and in the ratio of their partial pressure.

Dalton's Temperature Scale. This is a proposed temperature scale where a degree is defined as:

$$1°D = V_T - \frac{V_T}{273}$$

where °D = degrees Dalton

V_T = volume of a perfect gas at that temperature

Thus there is no absolute zero in this system but a minus infinity. Most physical laws are simpler if expressed in degree Kelvin.

Debye and Huckel Equation. This is an equation to determine the activity coefficient of an ion:

$$-\log A_i = Bn_i^2\sqrt{K}$$

where A_i = ion activity coefficient

$$B = \frac{2N^2e^3(\pi/1000)}{2303R^{3/2}(DT)^{3/2}}$$

N = Avogadro's number

D = dielectric constant of the solvent

e = electronic charge

n_i = valence of the ion

$K = \frac{1}{2}C_1n_i^2$

C_1 = number of gram ions per liter

T = temperature, °K

R = gas constant

De La Rue and Miller's Law. The expression form controlling sparkover voltage between two plates is given by:

$$d = \log_e f\left(\frac{V}{pd}\right) - \log_e g\left(\frac{V}{pd}\right)$$

where f = a function of the parenthesis
 V = voltage
 p = gas pressure
 d = distance between plates
 g = a function of the parenthesis

Dieterici Equation. The equation relates the pressure and volume of a real gas.

$$p = \frac{RT}{V - b} e^{-(a/RTV)}$$

where p = pressure
 R = gas constant
 V = gas volume
 a, b = experimental constants
 T = absolute temperature

At low pressures this reduces to van de Waals' equation.

Diffraction. This phenomena may be separated into two types:

1. Fraunhofer—that which occurs when the light source and screen are at infinite distance (or nearly so) from the aperture.

2. Fresnel—that which occurs when both source and screen are at a finite distance from the aperture.

Donnan Membrane Equilibrium. If an electrolyte containing two diffusible ions is separated by a membrane from a solution with a nondiffusing anion, the two constituent electrolytes will not diffuse equally through the membrane, but unequally, and this diffusion is dependent upon the concentration of the nondiffusing anion.

Dorn Effect. This is a variety of electrokinetic phenomena where when particles fall or settle in water, a potential difference is set up.

Draper Effect. When hydrogen and chlorine react, the volume of the resultant gas increases due to the heat generated. The volume increase is the Draper effect.

Drude's Theory of Conduction. The specific resistance of a substance is approximated by the equation:

$$\frac{1}{\rho} = \frac{1}{2} \frac{e^2 N}{m} t$$

where ρ = specific resistivity
 e = electronic charge
 N = number of free electrons per cc
 m = electron mass
 t = time for electron to move between collisions

Dufour Effect. This is the temperature gradient existing in a gaseous mixture as a result of an imposed concentration gradient. This combination of heat and mass transfer exists in an air-conditioning evaporator which is both cooling and dehumidifying the air.

Duhen-Margules Equation. This relates the relative proportions of two constituents in a system and their vapors.

$$X_A \frac{d \, (\log_e P_A)}{d \, X_A} = X_B \frac{d \, (\log_e P_B)}{d \, X_B}$$

or

$$\frac{d \, (\log_e P_A)}{d \, (\log_e X_A)} = \frac{d \, (\log_e P_B)}{d \, (\log_e X_A)}$$

where X_A = mole fraction of A

X_B = mole fraction of B

P_A = partial vapor pressure of A

P_B = partial vapor pressure of B

Duhring Rule. This relates the boiling temperature of two substances:

$$\frac{T_A - T_A{}'}{T_B - T_B{}'} = \text{constant}$$

where T_A = boiling point of A at pressure p

T_B = boiling point of B at pressure p

$T_A{}'$ = boiling point of A at pressure p'

$T_B{}'$ = boiling point of B at pressure p'

Earnshaw's Theorem. As a result of the Laplace field equations, it is stated that an electric potential cannot be a maximum or a minimum at a point not occupied by charges. Thus, a charged particle introduced in an electrostatic field cannot be in stable equilibrium.

Eberhardt Effect. This is the blurring at sharp image edges in a photograph due to the excitation of neighboring crystals by the light excited silver bromide crystals. Some of this blurring may also be due to the differential diffusion of the developer in the emulsion.

Einstein's Specific Heat Equation. This equation is:

$$C_v = 3R$$

where C_v = specific heat at constant volume

R = gas constant

This equation fails particularly at low temperatures so a Debye approximation is used where

$$C_v = 3R \left(\frac{\hbar v}{KT}\right)^2 \frac{e^{(\hbar v/KT)}}{[e^{(\hbar v/KT)} - 1]^2}$$

where $\hbar$ = Planck's constant

K = Boltzmann's constant

v = frequency of atomic oscillator

T = absolute temperature

Thus, deviations from the law of Dulong and Petit are due to a high frequency (v) of the Einstein atomic model.

Einstein Frequency. This is permissible frequency of atomic oscillation and is given by

$$v = 2.5 \frac{v^{1/6} \times 10^7}{M^{1/3}\beta^{1/2}}$$

where v = specific volume

M = atomic or molecular weight

β = compressibility

Einstein's Principle of Relativity. This consists of two important concepts:

1. That it is impossible by physical experiment to measure absolute motion of a body through space.

2. The measured velocity of light in space is constant and not related to the relative velocities of the source and observer.

Einstein-de Hass Effect. This is the angular momentum imparted to a free body by sudden magnetization.

Electrical Wind Effect. The corona discharge from an electrically-charged point (to a ring) causes a motion of the surrounding air away from the point for both a-c and d-c supplies.

Electrostatic Charges in Plastics. The static charge in plastics is a volume rather than a surface distribution.

Eotvos Rule. This equation is violated somewhat by most substances, but it states that the molar surface energy of all liquids is the same and also temperature invariant:

$$\frac{d\,\alpha(MV)^{2/3}}{dT} = K$$

where α = surface tension

M = liquid molecular weight

V = liquid specific volume

Esclangon Effect. This is the deviation of reflected light because of an oblique motion of the reflecting surface.

Faraday's Dark Space. This space is the nonluminous space between the positive column and the negative glow.

Fermats' Principle. If the path of a light ray from one point to another is reflected at a surface, the path taken is that requiring the least time. A similar law for refracted light sometimes leads to a maximum rather than a minimum time.

Fermi-Dirac Distribution. This expression gives the probability that an electron will exist at a given energy state.

$$f = \frac{1}{1 + e^{(E - E_f)/KT}}$$

where f = probability of electron at energy state E
E_f = energy of Fermi level
K = Boltzmann's constant
T = absolute temperature

Fermi Level (or Energy). If a substance were reduced to a temperature of absolute zero, all possible energy states below the Fermi level are occupied and all those above are empty of electrons. For some metals this is:

Metal	E_f (electron volts)
Na	3.1
Cu	7.0
Ag	5.5
Al	11.7

Fermi Temperature. The temperature dependence of energy and magnetic properties of a material near absolute zero is related to the Fermi temperature which is defined as:

$$T_F = E_F/K$$

where K = Boltzmann's constant
T_F = Fermi temperature
E_F = Fermi level

Ferrimagnetism. This name is sometimes applied to ferromagnetic behavior if the magnetic material contains a divalent Mn, Co, Ni, Cu, Mg, Zn, Cd ion and the general composition is $X^{2+} Fe_2^{3+} O_4$ where X is any one of the previous elements.

Ferroresonance. This is resonance in an L-C circuit where the inductance contains iron which reaches magnetic saturation sometime during operation.

Fitzgerald-Lorentz Contraction. An arm will contract in length, depending on its motion through space.

$$\frac{l}{l_0} = (1 - v^2/c^2)^{1/2}$$

where l = length of rod
l_0 = length of rod at rest
v = longitudinal rod velocity
c = velocity of light

Fletcher-Munson Effect. This is the loss of high- and low-frequency perception by the human ear as the sound intensity is decreased.

Foucault's Pendulum. A pendulum on the earth, if free to rotate, will rotate in the same plane as the earth rotates beneath it, giving an apparent change in the plane of rotation of the pendulum.

$$w = 15 \sin \phi$$

where w = angle of observed pendulum rotation per hour
ϕ = geographical latitude

Franck-Condon Principle. The energy emitted from an excited body is not the same as that absorbed as the lattice may shift, making the emitted frequency or energy slightly different from that absorbed.

Fraunhofer Lines. The dark lines observed in spectra of the sun. These are due to absorption by the gas of the upper atmosphere of the sun.

Fresnel-Arogo Laws of Polarized Interference. These laws relate interference and polarization:

1. Two rays will not interfere if polarized at right angles.

2. Two rays from the same source, if first polarized at right angles and then returned to the same plane, will interfere.

Fresnel Theory of Double Refraction. The double refraction of some crystals may be explained by the use of nonspherical wave fronts in the crystals.

Geiger Effect (or Ionization Effect). A light pulse is produced in some materials when a subatomic particle is stopped. The magnitude of this pulse is a linear function of the energy of the incident particle.

Geiger-Mueller Region. This is a region of operation for the counting tube of a Geiger counter. The output pulses produced by ionizing particles are independent of tube voltage over a wide range.

Gibbs Rule. This is a refinement of Dalton's law of partial pressure. The pressure of a gas mixture equals the sum of partial pressures only if the gases remain chemically free from each other.

Goldschmidt's Law. For primarily inorganic compounds, the crystal structure is fixed by the ratio of the numbers, the ratio of the sizes, and the polarization of the structural components.

Gough-Joule Effect. The absorption of heat during contraction of stretched rubber.

Grotthuss and Draper Law. Only absorbed radiation is effective for producing a chemical change in a substance.

Gudden-Pohl Effect. This is the momentary flash of light produced when an electric field is applied to or removed from a zinc sulfide phosphor during phosphorescence (afterglow).

Guldberg and Waage's Law is the same as law of mass action.

Grüneisen Constant. This is a constant, practically independent of temperature, which is useful in relating specific heats at constant temperature and volume.

$$C_p = C_v(1 + \gamma \alpha_v T)$$

and

$$\gamma = \alpha_v V / K C_v$$

also

$$\alpha_v = \frac{1}{V} \frac{\partial V}{\partial T}$$

$$K = -\frac{1}{V} \left[\frac{\partial V}{\partial p} \right]_T$$

where C_p = specific heat at constant pressure
C_v = specific heat at constant volume
γ = Grüneisen constant
α_v = volume expansion coefficient
T = absolute temperature
V = volume of material
K = compressibility
p = pressure

Haidinger Interference Fringes. These are fringes produced at infinity by light reflected from the two surfaces of a thick parallel—surface transparent plate.

Hallwock's Effect. This relates to the discharging action of ultraviolet light on a negatively-charged body.

Hartley Law. The total amount of information which can be transmitted by a system whose transmission is limited to a certain frequency range is proportional to the product of the frequency range times the time available for transmission.

Heisenberg Uncertainty Principle. The simultaneous determination of the velocity, any related property, and the position of a particle is impossible within a theoretical limit of error of

$$\Delta(mv)\ \Delta x = \hbar$$

where m = mass of particle
v = particle velocity
x = position
$\hbar$ = Planck's constant
Δ = increment of quantity

Heitler-London Convalence Theory. Two hydrogen atoms can combine only if the spins of their respective electrons are antiparallel. Thus covalent bonds are postulated to form only when two electrons with opposite spins are involved.

Herschel Effect. The developable density of the image on a photographic plate is lowered by re-exposure to longer wavelength radiation.

Hess Law. The energy change in a chemical action is equal whether the reaction occurs quickly or slowly or in steps.

Hydration Energy. Energy is liberated when readily soluble materials are dissolved in a solvent. The energy is

$$E = A\frac{e^2}{a_0}\left(1 - \frac{1}{n}\right) - \frac{1}{2}e^2\left(1 - \frac{1}{E}\right)\left(\frac{1}{R_+} + \frac{1}{R_1}\right)$$

where R_+ = radius of positive solution
R_1 = radius of negative solution
E = solvent dielectric constant
e = ion charge
n = Born repulsion exponent
a_0 = shortest interionic distance
A = Madelung constant

Since water has a high dielectric constant, this allows a large number of substances to liberate energy (negative E) upon dissolving, meaning water is a better solvent than most other liquids.

Huygen's Principle. Every point on a wave front may be considered as the center of a new wave and the resultant wave is produced by the interference of the new wavelets.

Hysteresis. Generally this is applied to losses resulting from non-symmetrical response with a symmetrical driving function. This occurs particularly in magnetic and ferroelectric circuitry as well as in mechanical devices.

Interference Coatings. Quarter wavelength films on a surface will cancel the reflection from that surface for the proper wavelength.

Jones Effect. The net surface tension of a salt solution first decreases as the salt concentration is increased, then increases as the normality of the solution is raised.

Joshi Effect. The mean current through an electrical discharge is decreased by external radiation.

Kirchhoff's Equations. These are the methods of determining the two specific heats of a gas.

$$\left[\frac{\partial(\Delta H)}{\partial T}\right]_P = C_P$$

$$\left[\frac{\partial(\Delta H)}{\partial T}\right]_V = C_V$$

where H = heat content of gas
T = gas temperature
P = gas pressure
V = volume
C = specific heat

Kirkendall Effect. This is a migration of atoms in a mixed crystal lattice. For a copper-brass system, the zinc diffuses out of the brass faster than the copper diffuses in.

Knight Effect. The frequency of nuclear resonance is greater for solid pieces of metal than for the same atoms in a chemical compound. This frequency increase is due to the local field produced by the paramagnetic behavior of the outer orbit electrons.

Konowaloff's Rule. The vapor above a mixture of two liquids is composed largely of that component whose vapor produced the greatest total pressure.

Kopp's Law. The molecular heat capacity of a solid compound is approximated by the sum of the atomic heat capacities of its constituents.

Lambert's Cosine Law. The illumination on a surface varies with the cosine of the angle of incidence.

Landau Diamagnetism. This diamagnetism is the contribution made by the free electrons to a metals magnetic susceptibility.

Landholt Fringe. With a bright light source, crossed Nicol prisms still do not give a completely dark field, but one which is crossed by a black fringe. This fringe changes position as the prisms are rotated and is due to the fact that the field produced by one Nicol prism is not uniformly polarized.

Langmuir Adsorption Theorem. Assuming a monomolecular adsorbed gas layer on the surface of an adsorber, the amount of gas adsorbed is

$$\frac{X}{M} = \frac{R_1 R_2 p}{1 + R_1 p}$$

where X = amount of gas adsorbed
          M = mass of adsorbent
    R_1, R_2 = constants for system
          p = gas pressure

Laplace's Equation. If no charges exist in a volume:

$$\nabla^2 E = \frac{\partial^2 E}{\partial X^2} + \frac{\partial^2 E}{\partial Y^2} + \frac{\partial^2 E}{\partial Z^2} = 0$$

where E = potential
   X, Y, Z = three coordinate directions

If, however, charges exist in the volume, the zero or the right side of the equation is replaced by an expression relating to the charge and its distribution.

Laplace's Sound Velocity Equation. This expression relates two specific heats and sonic velocity

$$V = \sqrt{\frac{C_p p}{C_v \rho}}$$

where V = velocity of sound in the gas
      C_p = specific heat at constant pressure
      C_v = specific heat at constant volume
      p = gas pressure
      ρ = gas density

Larmor's Formula. An accelerating electron radiates energy at the rate of:

$$W = \frac{2}{3} \frac{e^2}{c^3} \frac{dv}{dt}$$

where W = energy radiated
      e = charge on electron
      c = velocity of light
      v = electron velocity
      t = time

Larmor Precession. Under the influence of an external field, the plane of the electron's orbit in an atom precesses about the direction of the applied field. This precession produces an induced magnetic moment opposite to the applied giving rise to a diamagnetic behavior in the material.

Leisegang Rings. Some chemical precipitations may occur as a series of rings on films rather than as uniform reaction. An example is that produced by a drop of concentrated silver nitrate on a gelatin film.

Leonard Effect. If a water surface is disrupted so as to produce drops, these droplets will be charged with respect to the surrounding air. While the charge is normally negative, impurities affect the sign and amount.

London's Intermolecular Attraction. Even at absolute zero, molecules will possess energy. This is explained by assuming the electrons and nuclei in the molecules will act as dipoles, giving an intermolecular cohesive force.

Loschmidt Number. The number of molecules in 1 cc of gas at 0°C and standard pressure is:

$$L = \frac{N}{2.24 \times 10^4} = 2.7 \times 10^{19}$$

where L = Loschmidt Number
N = Avogadro's Number

Luxenburg Effect. This is the intermodulation of two radio stations of completely different frequencies in the Heaviside layer.

Maxwell's Law. Conductors carrying current in an electromagnetic system tend to deform so as to include the maximum number of lines of force.

Maxwell's Law (light). Light may be regarded as a very high frequency electromagnetic wave with electric and magnetic fields. The velocity of all electromagnetic waves being given by:

$$v = \frac{1}{\sqrt{\mu e}}$$

where v = wave velocity
μ = permeability of the medium
e = dielectric constant of medium

Meyer, Lothar Atomic Volume Curve. A periodicity is apparent if element atomic volume is plotted against their atomic number. The alkali metals are the highest and the transition elements the lowest.

Miller Effect. Multi-element vacuum tubes can give an effective capacitance gain or multiplication to a circuit.

Mirage Effect. This effect relates to the formation of inverted or deceptive images due to atmospheric refraction because of an air density change over a hot surface.

Misterlich Law of Isomorphism. Similar chemical formulas may be used to represent similar crystalline substances if they have similar chemical properties.

Moseley's Law. This law relates to the determination of atomic number by the use of X-ray diffraction techniques. The characteristic frequency of an element varies as the square of the atomic number.

Mott-Schottky Theory. This theory of semi-conductor rectification assumes that current carriers (holes and electrons) overcome the potential barrier between two materials by means of thermal excitation. The junction current is then approximated by:

$$I = A(e^{cV/KT} - 1)$$

where I = junction current

A = a constant (nearly)

c = charge on electron

V = applied junction potential

K = Boltzmann's constant

T = absolute temperature, °K

Madelung Constant. In a study of crystal binding energy, the energy of an ion in the crystal is given by

$$E = \frac{-Ae^2}{r}$$

where E = Coulomb energy of ion

A = Madelung constant

e = charge per ion

r = shortest interionic distance

For various materials the modelung constant are:

	A
Sodium chloride	1.747558
Cesium chloride	1.762670
Zincblende (ZnS)	1.6381

Magne-Crystallic Bodies. A material which is more easily magnetized in one direction than in another.

Malus' Law. A beam of light polarized by two successive reflections will have its intensity varied as the square of the cosine of the angle between the two reflecting surfaces. This law also gives the transmission of polarized light through a polarizing system.

$$I = I_0 \cos^2\theta$$

where I = intensity

I_0 = original intensity

θ = angle of rotation of polarizing medium

Mattheissen's Rule. The resistivity of a slightly impure metal is given as a function of temperature as:

$$\rho = \rho_0 + f(T)$$

where ρ = resistivity of sample

ρ_0 = constant, increases as impurities increase

$f(T)$ = temperature dependent, resistivity function

The usually applied form for metals is

$$\rho = \rho_0 + \alpha(T)$$

where α = temperature coefficient of resistance

T = temperature

Maxwell's Equations. Four general equations relate both electric and magnetic fields and the charges and currents which give rise to them:

$$\nabla \cdot \overline{D} = 4\pi\rho$$

$$\nabla \cdot \overline{B} = 0$$

$$\nabla \times \overline{\mathcal{E}} = -\frac{1}{c}\frac{\partial \overline{B}}{\partial t}$$

$$\nabla \times \overline{H} = \frac{1}{c}\left(4\pi i + \frac{\partial \overline{D}}{\partial t}\right)$$

where $\overline{D}$ = electric displacement flux density

ρ = charge density

$\overline{B}$ = magnetic flux density

$\overline{\mathcal{E}}$ = electric field intensity

t = time

$\overline{H}$ = magnetic field intensity

i = current density

c = velocity of light in free space

Nernst-Thompson Rule. The electrostatic attraction between anions and cations will be large in a medium of low dielectric constant and small if the solute has a high dielectric constant. Thus water forms extensively-ionized solutions.

Neumann's Formula. The mutual inductance between two circuits is given by:

$$M_{12} = \oint_1 \oint_2 \frac{\mu \, dl_1 \, dl_2}{r}$$

where M_{12} = mutual inductance
μ = permeability of the medium
r = distance between currents
l = vector element of current

The integration is to be performed for all the possible scalar products of dl_1 and dl_2.

Neumann's Law. The emf acting on a circuit is the battery voltage as well as an emf produced by a change in the tubes of magnetic induction enclosed by the circuit. More usually this is written

$$e = Ri + L\frac{di}{dt}$$

where e = applied voltage
R = circuit resistance
i = circuit current
L = circuit inductance
t = time

Newton's Equation for Velocity of Sound. The velocity of sound in a gas is given by

$$V = \sqrt{P/\rho}$$

where V = velocity of sound
P = pressure on medium
ρ = density of medium

This equation is true only as long as Boyle's law holds or at constant temperature. If the equation is changed to

$$V = \sqrt{\gamma(P/\rho)}$$

where γ = ratio of specific heats for constant pressure and volume,

the result is much more accurate (about $\frac{1}{3}\%$ versus 16%).

Newton's Law of Resistance. The resistance to a moving body by a medium is proportional to the square of the velocity for moderate velocities.

Newton's Rings. The interference colors produced by thin films of air between glass surfaces are termed Newton's rings or colors. This is especially true if a spherical lens is placed on a flat plate. Then rings are produced.

Newton's Theory of Light. Light is described as being a series of discrete bodies such as perfectly elastic balls which are propagated through space and react physically with optical materials to produce refraction and reflection.

Nuclear Magnetic Resonance. The angular momentum and charges possessed by atomic nuclei cause these nuclei to precess in a magnetic field. This also produces a splitting of the nuclear energy levels or the Zeeman effect. This precession and separation of the energy levels give a reasonance phenomenon similar to that with sodium light shining into sodium vapor.

Nucleus	Resonant Frequency (with 10^4 gauss field)
H^1	42.6 mc
Na^{23}	11.3
Cl^{35}	4.2

Ordered Alloys. If two metals are mixed, the sample resistivity versus percent added metal will increase ideally to a maximum and then decrease to the value for the pure second metal. If, however, the two materials form crystal compounds of definite composition, the resistance of these compositions will appear as minima in the otherwise smooth resistivity curve. The same phenomenon appears if a crystal lattice change occurs with a temperature change in a sample of fixed composition.

Ostwald Solubility Coefficient. This coefficient is the volume of gas dissolved in a unit volume of solute at a given temperature and pressure.

Page Effect. This is the click heard when iron is magnetized or demagnetized.

Paramagnetic Resonance. The angular momentum and charges carried by the electrons of an atom cause these electrons to precess and broaden the allowed energy levels. If potassium chloride (KCl) has excess potassium, the excess electrons will give a resonance 54 gauss wide, assuming a fixed a-c frequency and a variable field.

Parallax. The apparent displacement of an object when viewed from two different points.

Pasteur Effect. If a cell can break sugar down with and without oxygen, it will break down more in the absence of oxygen than with it.

Pauli Exclusion Principle. No two electrons in any atom may have the same four quantum numbers.

Pdotnikow Effect. This relates to the longitudinal scattering of light rays in a beam.

Photosynthesis. This is the process of building up chemical compounds with the aid of light, giving an end product which is of more complicated chemical structure or which possesses more energy. The most common example of this is the formation of sugars and starches from carbon dioxide and water by plants with the aid of light.

Piobert Effect. These are the long marks which appear on the surfaces of some metals in the direction of maximum shear stress after the metal has been deformed beyond its yield point.

Poiseulle's Formula. The quantity of fluid passing through a uniform capillary tube is:

$$m = \frac{\pi \rho r^2}{8\mu} \frac{P_1 - P_2}{l}$$

where m = mass of fluid
    ρ = fluid density
    r = capillary radius
    l = capillary length
    P = pressure on capillary ends
    μ = fluid viscosity

Poisson's Law. Under adiabatic expansion of a gas

$$PV^k = \text{a constant}$$

where P = gas pressure
    V = gas volume
    k = ratio of gas specific heats (constant pressure to constant volume)

Polarization by Scattering. When light energy is absorbed and reradiated by molecules, it is linearly polarized due to the force vibrations of the molecules. Thus, sunlight and daylight is partially linearly polarized by the atmosphere.

Prouts Hypothesis. This postulates that all atoms are composed of multiples of the hydrogen atom. The present idea is that the hydrogen nucleus does serve somewhat as such a building block.

Quenching Effect. If luminescent centers are too close together in a crystal, neither will function. Thus, there is an optimum concentration to secure the best luminescent efficiency.

Radiation Effect. If an n (donor) type germanium crystal is irradiated, the conductivity will first decrease. With more irradiation, the n type may be connected to p (acceptor) type and the conductivity may then increase.

Ramsauer Effect. The absorption of slow-moving electrons by materials in their paths.

Rayleigh's Law. The scattering of incident illumination is inversely proportional to the fourth power of the wavelength of the light.

Rayleigh Limit of Resolution. Primarily important for microscope objectives, the limit of resolution is:

$$d = \frac{0.61\lambda_0}{NA}$$

$$NA = \frac{\theta}{2n}$$

where d = limit of resolution in cm
λ_0 = wavelength of light in vacuum (cm)
NA = numerical aperture of the lens system
θ = angular aperture of objective
n = refractive index of material between objective and the lens

Rectification. This is the process of producing a uni-directional flow of electrons in an electric circuit. In semi-conductor-metal junctions, this action occurs because of a barrier of unneutralized immobile ions at the junction which stop almost all electron and hole flow across the junction. With applied voltages in one direction ($+$ on the n material) the effect of the barrier is decreased, while it is increased for the opposite polarity.

Remnant Polarization. In a ferroelectric material, after the applied electric field has been removed, the crystal polarization does not decrease to zero, but drops to a residual value. This is exactly analogous to residual magnetism. The effect has been utilized with electrets to produce long term electrostatic fields.

Restrike Phenomena. In electrical switchgear when two current carrying contacts are separated, the arc will eventually cease. If alternating current is employed and the arc ceased because of a current zero, the arc will restrike on the next half cycle if the applied voltage is high enough, and the current was great enough. This restriking is also affected by tip material and arc chute geometry; i.e., venting of the ionized gas. Orders of restrike voltage magnitude are: copper, 200 volts; silver, 500 volts.

Runge's Rule. For the Zeeman effect, the frequency shift is that of a Balmer line or a/b times this, where *a* and *b* are small integers.

Russel Effect. This is a chemical action in the absence of radiation on a photographic plate simulating that produced by radiation.

Singing Arc (also **Duddel Singing Arc**). If a radio-frequency arc is drawn between suitable electrodes, the carrier modulation (if audio frequency) is audible.

Sorensen pH Scale. This is a method of representing the concentration of the hydrogen ion in solutions:

$$pH = \log_{10} a_H{}^+$$

where pH = a number

$a_H{}^+$ = activity of the hydrogen ion

For dilute solutions, the hydrogen ion activity is the same as its concentration.

Soret Effect. A concentration gradient is established in a gaseous mixture if a temperature gradient exists. The heavier molecules usually diffuse to the lower temperature. A similar phenomenon exists in liquids.

Stark-Einstein Law. In a light or radiation induced chemical reaction, each molecule absorbs a quantum of radiation.

Stark-Luneland Effect. A beam of light is polarized by a beam of moving atoms.

Steiner's Theorem. The moment of inertia of a body varies according to the axis of rotation.

$$I_X = I_c + Mx^2$$

where I_X = moment of inertia about arbitrary axis

I_c = moment of inertia of body about axis parallel to I_X and passing through the center of gravity of the body

M = mass of the body

x = shortest distance between arbitrary axis and axis through centroid of the body

Superposition Theorem. For most applications of fluid, sound, or electromagnetic waves, the displacement or intensity at any point is equal to the sum of those of the individual waves.

Sabattier Effect. This is the partial solarization of a photographic negative. The process is:

Normal exposure.
Develop two-thirds normal time.
Expose to light.
Develop one-third normal time.

Saturation Magnetization. When an increasing magnetic field is applied to a ferromagnetic material, the resultant flux in that material will increase rapidly to the saturation point. Above this point, the flux will increase only slowly, and eventually only as rapidly as though the material were air or vacuum. Some saturation points are given.

Solid	Saturation Magnetism (cgs at Room Temperature)
Fe	1707
Co	1400
Ni	485
MnAs	670
MnSb	710

Schottky Effect. An electron near a metal-vacuum or metal-gas boundary feels an attractive force toward the metal, or an image potential in the metal. Thus an electron normally must obtain enough energy to penetrate this boundary in order to escape. The Schottky effect is the apparent reduction in this work function by an applied external electric field.

Shenstone Effect. This is the increased photoelectric emission of some metals after the passage of an electric current.

Temperature Effects. As a by-product of a theory by Arrhenius, it may be stated as a rule of thumb that the speed of any chemical reaction doubles for each 10°C rise in temperature. This crude rule also applies to the life of insulation and the self-discharge rates of storage batteries.

Temperature-induced free electrons in flame gases will absorb high-frequency radio waves.

Thermodielectric Effect (Costa Ribeiro Effect). Upon the solidification of some dielectrics, negative charges are expelled from the solid to the liquid phase. The charges are thus nonuniformly distributed.

Thermoluminescence. When luminescent centers in a phosphor are activated, but the phosphor temperature is low, little glow actually occurs. If the phosphor temperature is now gradually raised, a temperature will be reached where the glow is a maximum. This emission of light produced by a temperature increase in a previously excited phosphor is termed thermoluminescence.

Tolman Effect. If a conductor is accelerated, a potential will be developed across the conductor due to electron inertia.

Trouton's Law. The ratio of the molar latent heat of vaporization of a liquid divided by its boiling point at atmospheric pressure is a constant for all liquids.

Tunnel Effect. Under certain conditions with metal semi-conductor boundaries and very thin barrier layers (about 10^{-7} cm) the electrons are transported through the barrier rather than over the barrier.

Tyndall Effect. Particles in a fluid, gas, or transparent media are readily seen if the media is viewed against a dark background and at right angles to the light beam.

Van der Waals' Adsorption. The adsorption of a gas by a solid may be brought about by molecular cohesion. This type of adsorption may be distinguished by its reversibility, the speed with which equilibrium is attained, and by the low energy involved.

Van't Hoff Osmotic Pressure Equation. For a dilute solution:

$$PN = kT$$

where P = osmotic pressure
N = solution dilution
T = absolute temperature
k = constant nearly equal to gas constant

If the solution contains an electrolyte, the equation becomes

$$PN = iRT$$

where i = van't Hoff factor
and

$$i = a(n - 1)$$

where a = degree of dissociation
n = number of molecules per volume of electrolyte

Van't Hoff Superposition Principle. The optical rotary power of a material containing asymmetrical carbon atoms is equal to the algebraic sum of the rotations caused by each carbon atom alone, and is independent of the rest of the molecular structure.

Vegard's Law. When two similar metals form solid solutions in all proportions, a typical lattice dimension varies uniformly with change of composition from that of one constituent to that of the other. Negative as well as positive deviations can be observed, however.

Villard Effect. If a sensitized photographic plate is exposed to X-rays, its subsequent sensitivity to white light is decreased.

Voigt Effect. Light is doubly refracted when passing through a vapor in a strong perpendicular magnetic field.

Wehnelt Interruptor. If two electrodes of widely different sizes are immersed in an electrolyte, and sufficient current is passed between these electrodes, the current is interrupted as rapidly as 1800 times per second.

Weiss Hypothesis. This is the foundation of ferromagnetic theory:

1. A ferromagnetic material consists of microscopic regions (domains), each permanently magnetized. The complete material has a magnetic field determined by the vector sum of the contributions by all the domains.

2. Within each domain the magnetization is due to a parallel alignment of all the atomic dipoles.

Workman-Reynolds Effect. If a sample of water contains a small proportion of certain salts, electrical potentials are developed when the water is in the process of freezing.